"Watch Me!"

Connecting to Your Child Through Play

The QUICK, SIMPLE, on the go GUIDE that teaches you how to Connect, Grow and Learn with your child in minutes a day!

Cherina L. Williams, M.Ed., CCC-SLP
Licensed Pediatric Speech and Language Pathologist

First Print:
ISBN: 978-1-7345206-1-3 (paperback)
ISBN: 978-1-7345206-2-0 (Ebook)

www.iheartspeechtherapy.com
www.ivegotthiskid.com

Printed in the United States of America

Table Of Contents

CONCLUSION   **40**

Foreword

As an emergency room physician, I have the privilege of treating some amazing children and adults who come to the hospital with a wide variety of medical concerns. Though our treatment practices have expanded over the years to include state-of-the-art tools and new algorithms, one feature remains the linchpin in diagnosing a complicated medical condition: communication. A simple conversation with face-to-face interaction seems to magically unlock the problems that exist beneath the surface. It is the single skillset that I have found most helpful, and at the same time, least utilized in day-to-day settings.

For most adults, communication and its role outside of goal-oriented interaction is poorly understood. Rather than play, communication almost serves a strict functional purpose: "Get X to accomplish Y." This is largely a by-product of our adult lives, driven by urgency, efficiency, and task resolution. However for children, play itself has a much different utility. It is the perfect medium for multi-level learning. It becomes the conduit for social interaction and exploration. Play also helps orient and catalogue various stimuli, and aids in the development of confidence, creativity and problem-solving abilities.

This book challenges our contextual understanding of communication as it relates to childhood play. Adults will find that their own communication abilities are an untapped resource that can elevate interactive experiences for their children. Further, communication will be solidified as a vital part of the play regimen. And just as this skillset improves my connection with patients, it will also amplify any parent's relationship with their child–allowing them to grow together.

Dr. Italo M. Brown, Emergency Room Physician, Stanford Medical Center

Preface

In my experience, play-based therapy has proven to be the most successful way to encourage and elicit the acquisition of new language. Over the years, I've picked up on patterns and noticed the questions asked most often by parents as well as the areas where I provide the most advise, collaboration and feedback. If we want our little one to reach his or her fullest potential, some of these areas may need to be addressed in order to get the ball rolling. All it takes to maximize play is recognizing your child's play style, communication patterns and what makes them connect with you and the world around them. From there, a few simple tweaks will facilitate the foundation for you both to step into amazing play.

In this book, I share my exciting journey to answer important questions from parents about communicating and interacting with their children using a simple, yet comprehensive tool to enhance the quality of play. Many parents and children who enter my office have not bonded due to difficulties with communication. They seek my expert skills as a speech and language pathologist to bridge the gap, changing a reluctant speaker into a communicator who is confident enough to share thoughts and ideas. Quite simply, I have learned that nothing is more exhilarating than changing the scope of a parent's and child's relationship using language. Simultaneously, children become confident about expressing themselves, while parents become allies, nurturing language development. Both parent and child appear more at ease when interacting with each another. It is my goal to reach as many families as possible with this book, in order to bridge the gap from limited verbal interaction to blissful reciprocal communication.

Cherina L. Williams, M.Ed., CCC-SLP, Licensed Pediatric Speech and Language Pathologist

Introduction

Communication is a gift and an honor. Sending our thoughts and receiving feedback takes a lot more effort and energy than we acknowledge. For most people, communication comes naturally, while for others, it requires more time and thought. Research has proven that early remediation of speech and language delays prepares children to compete with same-age peers by the time they enter kindergarten (Cortese, 2017; Sualy, et al, 2011).

Establishing early language is the platform for social skills, pre-literacy, reading and writing. Falling behind in language development can have dramatic short- and long-term effects. As parents, providers and nurturers in our children's lives, it is our duty to provide opportunities for early language skills to ensure long-term success. What does typical language use sound like?

With infants, it starts with joint attention (looking and paying attention to each other), "motherese" (speaking in a melodic tone to your baby), and babbling (mama, dada, baba). By 18 to 24 months, the language boom occurs, with toddlers gaining anywhere from five to seven new words each week. Our young explorers now have the physical mobility to roam, graze, touch, learn, feel and do. They also have the fine motor capability to turn sounds into words, thereby establishing early language skills. For the past couple of years, your child has overheard each and every word you've said, creating a collection. Now, it is their time to put them into use. If your child is exhibiting difficulties putting words into use, some changes may need to be made on both your and your child's part (no, it is not your fault–I do not play the blame game).

It takes two to tango, just as it takes two to communicate. And because we are the adults, we have to meet our children at the level where they learn best, which is through play.

part one

Preparing for Amazing Play

Now that you have basic information about typical language acquisition, let's roll up our sleeves and take action steps to support that process.

1. De-clutter the Play Area

Sometimes we give our children too many options during play, which leaves limited opportunity to attend to a specific toy or activity. While it is great to have variety, a playroom that looks like a toy store is often overwhelming and makes appropriate play and exploration super difficult. If it is an option, limit your play area to five accessible toys. Label and place additional toys in cabinets, cubbies, and closets where they are out of sight. Personally, I am a huge fan of cabinets with doors and cubbies. (Stores such as IKEA, Target and now even Dollar Stores can help de-clutter and organize your space.)

If you need design inspiration or organization techniques, websites like Pinterest provide great creative spaces that help with all sizes.
Or seek the help from a friend or family member.
Having another set of eyes on the same space can produce different ideas.

Please see Section 19 for additional ideas. on toy access.

2.   Start Play Simple

 For most adults, good old fashion play using toys such as blocks, balls, dolls, action figures, drawing and Play Doh© is a thing of the past. As a result, parents almost have to revisit a vulnerable place to allow inhibitions to come down and simply play. With that being said, you can help to get yourself comfortable with the routine. Start playing with your child for no more than five to ten minutes daily. You would be surprised how much can be accomplished during that time. Depending on the activity, you can play with up to two toys in five minutes or three to four toys in ten minutes.

If you are wondering whether five to ten minutes is enough time, keep in mind that you are building up the quality of play. Spending more time is encouraged if positive engagement is occurring on both sides. More importantly, if you are new to play or changing old habits, it is best to acclimate yourself in smaller quantities to keep the play morale going.

If you notice that your child is exhibiting difficulties focusing on two toys during five minutes of play, maybe a personal goal is to build their attention and focus. For instance, if Timmy goes from one toy to the next in seconds, try changing the atmosphere (i.e., turn off the television, use a quiet voice, turn off the lights, and try to eliminate any distractions that may stop play).

3. Have Fun

♥ Play should never feel like a chore. It should be fun, engaging, energizing and fulfilling. Play is the first step to building a strong relationship with your child. Taking the time to engage in play demonstrates you are genuinely enjoying time together, while promoting and fostering a strong, healthy relationship. Perfection is not key here—fun is! As long as you keep it fun, you are establishing a firm foundation that will last a lifetime.

You might be wondering, "What if I had a bad day? Should I avoid play?" Everyone experiences days that seem to hold a massive gray rain cloud overhead, while it is really a nice sunny day for everyone else. This is life. However, over the years, I have learned that sitting down for play is a mood booster. Listening and observing little ones and their discoveries can turn any cloudy day into a sunny one, if you allow it. In fact, having fun with your little one can change your day's entire trajectory.

4. Follow Your Child's Lead

Have you ever been a part of a conversation in which it becomes obvious in the first two minutes that you will not get a word in edge wise? Pretty boring, right? You probably zoned out after the first minute and then started doing your own thing or looking for a way out by the second minute. Children are the same in this way. Yes, they may be small, but they are people. As soon as they feel like you are monopolizing their play, they are likely to check out and move on.

For example, if your child is driving a car up and down a slide, grab a car and join in. Don't try to convince them that your idea of making the car fly is much better. Don't try to probe for the car color or the sound the car makes. The more you meet your child at their level, the more they allow their guard to come down, making play more open and fun.

5.   Life is Not a Quiz

Imagine your worse subject in school. Imagine someone always quizzing you on that subject. You would probably fail every time. The same holds true for kiddos with expressive language delays (or 'sluggish speakers'). If your child is not comfortable speaking, why place pressure on them to perform? Make it a conversation, or even better, feed them the information and allow them to naturally imitate you. For example, if you are playing with shapes, rather than saying, "What shape is this?" try making it conversational. "Square. Look, Ella, I have the square," or, "Blue square. Blue square in." You will be surprised how much your little one begins to imitate you once emphasis is placed on what you want them to acknowledge, without the question.

6. Limit the Number of Words

 Talk—please talk. Be cognizant of the length of your sentences when speaking to your child. If your child has an expressive language delay (or is a 'sluggish speaker'), it is probably best to use no more than two to three words per utterance.

After they begin using two to three words, you can bump it up by using one or two additional words. For some children, comprehension may be fine, and they just require additional time for motor programming of their articulators (lips, tongue, teeth, hard and soft palate, jaw). For other kiddos who exhibit difficulties understanding language, we want to make our messages clear and simple to follow. If you go over their heads, you have pretty much lost them. So try to keep their attention by using simple phrases.

Consider:

"Come, Ella, sit down," while using a beckoning gesture, instead of, "Come over here, Ella, and sit down next to me."

Your child is more likely to follow, and later, to imitate a shorter, direct message.

part two

Stepping Into Amazing Play

In this section, we'll move from preparing a space for play to specific approaches to use with your child.

7. Employ Toy Control

I love play. I love toys. If I didn't, I would be in the wrong field ...however, I can say that there is nothing less fun than having a toy fly at your head from what feels like an Oakland A's pitcher. This is where toy control comes in. At times, it is necessary to hoard objects to ensure that all parties stay safe. For example, if you are enjoying blocks, there is no need to dump the entire bag. It can become overwhelming and leaves you vulnerable for a toy being chucked at you, stepped on or lost. Start with one to two blocks each and then build from there. Add a single block at a time. Same with puzzles, play people or action figures, cars, balls, etc. Place a majority of toys either behind you or to your side, where they are easily accessible to you, but not to your child. This also gives both you and your child the opportunity to label the toy, demonstrating object actions and to work on requesting, eye contact, joint attention and focus. For our little ones who demonstrate difficulties enjoying play with others, making all parts of a toy accessible reinforces their attention on the toy, rather than on you.

8.   How Do I Engage a 'Play Runner?'

I often hear, "When I try to play with my child, they run away." Sometimes, you can genuinely do all the things listed above and your child is just "not that into you." Honestly, it's not you. Play and language are simply too abstract, and it is too difficult to predict what is going to happen next. In some cases, your child may have attention, focus or sensory difficulties that make it challenging to sit down for any period of time.

There are things that you can do to try and help your play runner. Sit down and place the toy in front of you. Begin to play alone. Don't look at your play runner, just have fun. In some cases, you don't have to speak. Just play. More often than not, your play runner will want to know what is happening and possibly come over to join you. If they do, keep playing and quietly invite them to play with you by handing them the object. If they don't approach you, try another toy

A 'play runner' is a child who prefers to play independently, avoiding contact with peers, parents and siblings and resists participating in play with others.

Ultimately, their goal is to avoid contact and interaction during play.

after one minute. That activity may not be highly stimulating. If and when they move on, it is okay. They are probably telling you with their body that they are done with that activity. Pull another activity out and start the process again.

Incorporating visual images of toys and objects is an additional method parents can use to invite their child into play. This is a dirty version of what speech and language pathologists call Picture Exchange System, or PECS. PECS is a great way to encourage your child to communicate with you their wants and needs for specific objects. It eliminates the demand of any expressive language pressure.

If your goal is to reinforce expressive language or teach expressive language, you can use a few other helpful aids in the process. I am personally a huge fan of sign language (see text box for more information). It is a great bridge for teaching language while providing a physical, tangible model of simple words that are functional to your child's life. If your child is not using at least 10 words by 18 months, incorporating simple signs may help ease the frustration and build the foundation of strong communication. Signs I gravitate towards when teaching early language include: more, all done, please, want, help, no/yes. These very simple signs can generalize into a number of settings and situations while your child is learning how to use spoken language.

Nowadays, there are a number of American Sign Language (ASL) resources readily available without having to commit to a sign language course. ASLpro.cc, signingsaavy.com and handspeak.com are great resources. If you feel like you have mastered these resources and would like to continue learning ASL, try seeking sign language courses through your local community college.

9. Use Descriptive Play (aka Parallel Play)

💬 For our little ones who demonstrate a hard time understanding language or how to use language, we can use parallel play. The label appears more complicated than the actual definition. Parallel play simply means describing our child's actions during play. For example, if a car is going up and down the slide, we simply say, "Up, up, up," or, "Car up." If they are rolling the ball, we say, "Roll the ball," or, "Roll." The goal is to keep our descriptions super simple, attach a label to what they are demonstrating and provide a language model they can attempt to imitate. It also reinforces that we as parents are attending to and are very interested in their actions during play.

10. Don't Turn Your Back on Me

During play, ideally, you and your child will be facing each other. Or you can sit at a 90-degree angle. This is an important part of play for a few reasons. If your child has their back facing you during play, it is hard to promote togetherness, play modeling, attention, etc. It also leaves your child in a place where they are essentially playing alone. If your child exhibits an expressive language delay, it is hard to model language when their back is facing you. Also, for many of our little ones

If it appears your child is not attending, lightly tap the toy on their arm, or place the toy on your nose, to gain eye contact. Each instance of eye contact should be about three seconds long. Toddlers can attend from two to eight minutes, depending on the activity and the age: younger children, shorter attention span.

who aren't using their words, it becomes important to understand that children use their bodies to communicate.

If you are looking at their back, it will become a difficult task to pick up on their non-verbal cues (i.e., frowning, smiling, happy, unsure, etc.). In order to promote opportunities for your child to face you, try placing the toy of interest in front of you. Have your child sit in front of you so that both are facing the toy and can look at one another. Or, if your child is already on the floor playing and you would like to join in, sit directly in front of your child and the toy. If your child takes the toy and moves it away, try either sitting at a 90-degree angle, or put the toy back between you and your child.

11. Understand 'Crash-and-bang' Play

Until this section, I have advised you to follow your child's lead and to join in play. However, there is an exception to the rule. This is when you observe 'crash-and-bang' play. Crash-and-bang play is a type of interaction that involves repetitiously making two objects erratically collide for long periods of time. You may notice that the child begins to move more erratically as the objects make contact. You may also notice your little one may not be attending to the two objects colliding.

Remember, play promotes actions and behavior familiar to your child's world. You play kitchen to cook and feed people, babies are rocked and fed, animals live in different habitats and cars are driven, and, sometimes, they crash. If you notice your child engaging only in crash-and-bang play with every toy, it may be time to interject and model how to play with toys appropriately (refer to Section 10: Don't Turn Your Back on Me). If you notice the crash-and-bang play begins to become more erratic, it may be time to peacefully shift to another activity. Make sure you have the next activity readily available, so that the transition to the next activity will be smooth.

Why discourage crash-and-bang play?

Crash-and-bang play is discouraged because it limits what a child can learn during play. If they are resorting only to crash-and-bang play, then only "cause and effect play" is nurtured. Cause and effect occurs when our toddlers use one object to make simple outcomes occur with another object (see cde.cd.gov). This play is observed with infants during their early play development.

For example, you may remember your infant sitting in a highchair and hitting the spoon on the table repetitively while cracking up. As our infants become toddlers, we expect their cause and effect play to mature. The cause and effect play now has an outcome they are attending to. For example, we may see our toddler cry every time mom or dad drops them off for daycare, or the toddler may use different pots to make different, specific sounds.

We want to expand imagination, vocabulary, attention and focus during play. But crash-and-bang play does not promote enhancing play skills—unless you are pretending to drive on the road and accidentally crash. You can then expand the crash play by inviting the ambulance, peace officers and doctors on the scene. You can also work on emotions by asking, "Are you okay?"

part three

During Amazing Play, Keeping the Momentum Going

Okay, now we've addressed preparing and approaching play. Now let's look at how parents can keep up the momentum.

12. Listen to Calming Melodies

♥ Isn't it funny how some children wake up in the morning and move until their brain and body completely shut down into sleep mode? For the first hour of the day, this behavior seems cute, fun and amazing; however, as the day progresses, it can become exhausting. It is fascinating to watch how active our little ones can be, yet this can also create play conflict for the parent seeking to join in the fun and have one-on-one time.

Recently, I have integrated classical music into sessions for my kiddos who are constantly moving. The results are tremendously rewarding (Mori, Naghsh & Tezuka, 2011; Schellenberg, 2005). I have watched children who have initially demonstrated difficulty sitting longer than two minutes increase their playtime with me to 20 minutes or longer! By providing your little one a background melody, the brain can passively focus while actively engaging in play.

13. Choose an Appropriate Tone and Rate of Speech.

There is nothing more hilarious than a parent who speaks to their child with a rate of speech slower than a turtle with three legs. Not only do most children flee from the parent, but I also often notice these children are a bit more irritable. In most cases, your little ones understand more than you think. Using a melodic tone with a normal rate of speech should suffice. In addition, your goal is to elicit imitations, and the last thing you want to reinforce is your child using a rate of speech that is not within the norm.

Does this contradict Section 6: Limit Your Words During Play? Absolutely not! There is a difference between using fewer words versus choosing an appropriate tone and rate of speech. You can use an appropriate number of words when speaking to your toddler at an appropriate rate. Also, keep in mind that if you personally limit what you think your little sugar knows, they may be reluctant to showcase their full abilities.

part four

Communication Tips to Use During Play

Because enhancing communication is our primary focus, let's zero in on specific tips and techniques.

14. Be Honest

Timmy was hitting his mother and attempting to get her attention. His vocabulary included fewer than five words, and so he was frustrated that he could not get his messages across. Mom started turning red, and her tone with Timmy went from friendly to agitated. Timmy had a tantrum, and Mom became angry. The next time this occurred, I asked Mom to let Timmy know, "No thanks to hitting. Show me what you want." (Yes, I know it is more than two or three words, but we wanted to decrease negative behavior.) Even a gentle touch while saying, "I don't like that," is totally appropriate.

We live in a society where parents are perceived as villains for saying, "No," in order to redirect a behavior. Redirecting behavior is actually positive for your little one as long as you are providing a solution to the problem. Toddlers will not be babies forever, and if hearing, "No" for the first time happens on the playground, then they may be in for a few rough weeks of school.

Children don't always need to be distracted to deter a behavior; they need to understand from a real place, at their own level, why something is or is not agreeable. This starts with you, at home, being honest with them. Although there may be some push back from Timmy, do not worry. Timmy will be okay with you redirecting his behavior with a solution (even if he isn't, we have to start somewhere). You will probably be happier when he is trying to use words rather than his body to communicate with you. And, even if he is not, you were able to express yourself honestly and wholeheartedly. He is learning from you how to interact.

Using "no" to redirect unwanted behavior is perfectly acceptable.

The "not optional" (aka "No") strategy helps you decide how to appropriately employ that term.

That way, your little sugar understands that when you use the word "no" it means something is completely off limits, or "not optional."

24

15. Be Direct

🗨 Imagine being in the company of a good friend at dinner. Imagine your friend takes off their shoe at the table and begins to cut their toenails. Rather than politely advising the friend to stop, would you say, "Look, there is a rocket ship coming our way," to distract their attention? Now put that friend in place of your child, who is also demonstrating behavior that is not very becoming. Rather than distract your toddler, it is best to exercise honesty to avoid the behavior in the future.

Distracting behavior stops the action for that brief moment, yet it does not teach the child appropriate versus inappropriate behavior. If your child is not listening to your words, providing physical models is often helpful to help facilitate your desired outcome. It is okay to express displeasure to your child in order to help them learn appropriate social skills and to provide a model exhibiting how to respond with words over behaviors. Like anything else, it may take a few trials to get used to; just remember, Rome wasn't built in a day.

Remember:

Honesty is the best method to form a strong relationship. Being direct not only redirects unwanted behavior in a kind, firm manner, it also provides teachable moments about why certain behaviors are not acceptable. Taking advantage of these moments teaches empathy and healthy citizenship.

16. Pass the Passy

In infancy, pacifiers are used to soothe and quiet an uncomfortable child in an uncomfortable situation. As your little one begins moving around, increasing in sound play, imitations, and eventually first words, the pacifier outgrows its usefulness. Now, there may be an attachment to the little rubber friend that has calmed potential disasters; however, as parents, we have to decide the role of a pacifier as your little one moves from infancy to toddler.

By 12 months, your child should be weaned from using the pacifier during waking hours. "Why?", you may ask. Let me tell you: if your sugar has something lodged in their mouth, it makes it difficult to get any sounds or words out. Or you may notice your child talking from the side of the pacifier. Either way, it is not a great way to establish early language.

Allowing your child to use their pacifier after a certain age is not great for their oral-motor development. By 24 months, your child is not only at the language boom, but their articulators are also continuing to develop. The pacifier is helping shift their hard palate up, and causes potential misalignment for their teeth. As much as I love my dentist, I would hate to spend extra money for braces in the future.

The pacifier takes away amazing opportunities for your child to communicate his or her ideas. Imagine having an ice cube in your mouth during the day. After a while, the bother of trying to talk may not be worth it because of the challenge moving the ice around. It is pretty much the same for your child with a pacifier. It is a lifesaver for some families with infants that eventually becomes a nightmare for toddlers, who should be using valuable waking hours to communicate.

Now, I understand that you have been tasked with what seems like the impossible, and yet, nothing is impossible. You can do this! In order to start the weaning process of the pacifier, it's wise to let your toddler know that the pacifier is going to begin taking a "break during the day." If your toddler becomes uneasy, reassure your little sugar that the pacifier will be a nap time and nighttime friend. If you notice that does not work, use your stealthy parenting powers to hide the pacifier throughout the day in a place that is inaccessible. Bring it out during resting times and see if that does the trick.

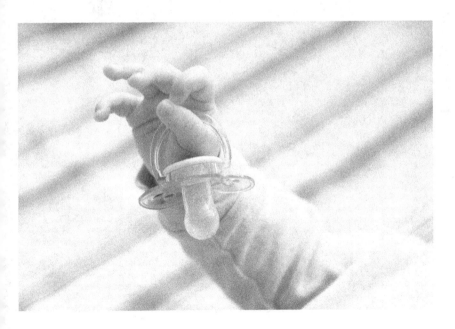

part five

Strategies to Step Into Amazing Story Time

We all enjoy good stories. Read on to find out how they can be incorporated into playtime.

17. Read to me.

There is nothing more fulfilling than picking up a good book, or even listening to a good book for that matter. Loving books is something that can be taught with practice. Do not get me wrong; some little ones naturally love story time, which is a big "YAY" for the parents of that child. One of the most common things I hear from parents is, "I try to read, but Timmy won't listen," or, "They are not interested in story time." That is okay! Story time can be a fun time to have amazing play with your child. And guess what: it is okay if they do not want to hear the entire story word-for-word. Like play, story time should be low pressure and fun. When coaching my parents on building great story time skills, I start with the following questions:

Remember:

New to reading with your little sugar?

No problem!

To get the ball rolling, try shorter, more simplistic stories or nursery rhymes. That way, you can practice these techniques, while building attention, listening skills and vocabulary.

Who is in control of the book during story time? I ask because many little ones are page-flipping masters. If they have full possession of the book, it becomes difficult for mom or dad to read even the title of the book. It is also hard to explore pages or read any words. If you are able to control the book, you eliminate the 'page flipping machine' taking over.

Grab masters. Little ones have little, cute hands that enjoy grabbing everything. This behavior is typical and can get in the way of exploring a really great book. To avoid grab masters from taking over (if it is an issue), simply place your hand at the bottom of the book (one hand on each page), make sure your fingers are facing the front of the book, and hold the book in a place where your child can see the book, but cannot take possession the book. If your adorable grab master attempts to take over, simply flip your wrist down like a 360-degree circle and the little fingers will automatically lose their grip.

Is your book too sophisticated? In this day and age, society teaches us that our children need to be "ahead of the game" or at the "top" of everything. Unbeknownst to us, we put unnecessary pressure on our children, and frankly, we take the fun out of everything. Ensure the stories chosen are age-appropriate for the child. Do not worry, as little Einstein will eventually arrive at Shakespeare. Remember, Dr. Seuss is still as amazing and relevant as he was 40 years ago. If you are able to choose age-appropriate books that are attention-grabbers, chances are your little one will begin to love story time.

Word-for-word. Page scanning can be just as fulfilling as reading the entire story. In fact, when you are able to look at pages together with your child, chances are, you are likely to see more participation from them. It is okay to read just one page and scan the rest of the book. For example, if you are reading a story such as "The VERY HUNGRY Caterpillar," not only can you work on the metamorphosis of a caterpillar turning into a butterfly, but you can also engage in pretend play (i.e., eating new foods introduced on each page), following directions (i.e., "turn the page") or simply colors.

part six

Parent Portal to Track Progress

You're doing great! Keeping track of your progress can help to encourage you and your child. In addition to reading this section, see Appendix A for journaling ideas to guide you along the way.

18. Journal About Your Progress

Remember, where you start does not dictate where you will finish. Journaling the play process is a healthy way to keep track of your progress. It also provides a space to reflect and identify any areas of difficulty. There is no right or wrong way to express yourself, and your thoughts do not have to be shared with anyone. At times, journaling eliminates the need to question, "Is this working?" By identifying milestones, you can eliminate any feelings of self-doubt. Reflecting on what you accomplish in a day, a week, or a month can keep the momentum up. In addition, if there are any gaps in using these tools, journaling can demonstrate any regression in joint play. This tool can help you get through the process honestly and wholeheartedly.

What is ASHA? The American Speech-Language-Hearing Association is a national association for licensed speech and language pathologists. Each state has individual associations that represent local speech-language pathologists, providing parenting resources and presenting current topics relating to speech and language pathology.

Children are amazing explorers who love to learn from their environments. Strategically modifying how you engage can enhance your and your child's interaction. The foundation provided for early language development will have a lasting effect on future social and academic abilities. If you find that trying these methods requires more support and guidance, find a local licensed speech and language pathologist through www.asha.org or your state speech and language association.

19. Improve Toy Access to a Variety of Toys

Over the past 18 steps, I've mentioned aspects of how to tweak play with your child, to shift from questions to conversation, to enhance story time and to journal about your progress. Not only is it essential to the success of my suggestions to make adjustments that fit your lifestyle, but it is just as important for families to have access to quality toys. If you live in a big city, as I do, toy access may or may not be as challenging; however, if you live in an environment where access to toys and stores are limited, please keep reading.

There are many options for gaining access to toys. Toy subscriptions are readily available that start at as little as $19.99 monthly. (For a list of some toy subscription options, check out Appendix F.) They even offer discounts for longer subscription commitments. The flexibility in these programs is amazing, as some allow you to return toys that are not a fit for your little ones. The benefit of these services is that you can pick and choose what you like for your child, and some of these services have an option to trade toys monthly, so that you can have variety. This also declutters your play area without massive cleaning parties on your part. And because ongoing access to new toys are being provided, you and your child will never be bored with the same toys.

Lending libraries are another best kept secret for great toys! The wonderful part about lending libraries is the variety of toys provided for free. If "free" is not enough of an incentive, or if you are trying to figure out the type of toys your child gravitates toward, this is a wonderful method to learn what they enjoy. Most importantly, the toys go back after so many weeks, which, once again, keeps your play space from being cluttered.

Now, if lending libraries and toy subscriptions are not your scene, do not fret. You may want to build up your toy collection to have a few staple toys on hand. I'm all for that. However, if you don't have a huge budget, but you still want quality toys, try donation centers (Goodwill, Salvation Army, Savers, Habitat for Humanity and so on). When on maternity leave with my son, our household budget was cut in half, which meant my variable spending was cut down as well. I have personally found some amazing books and toys for a discounted price. In fact, some of the items were barely used and in new packaging. I still visit these stores when searching for some items or when my children want to shop on a limited budget.

Other great places to access toys on a limited budget are discount department stores (such as Ross, Home Goods, Tuesday Morning, Marshalls and TJ Maxx). It is important to know exactly what you are looking for when shopping in these types of stores. Children's books, Legos©, dolls, doll accessories and puzzles are usually the best finds. Again, a small budget will go a long way. That is important for toddlers, as milestones are met at a rapid pace.

The final suggestion for toy searching is your community. Never be afraid to ask friends or relatives with older kids if they have any toddler toys they want to be relieved of. My in-laws personally furnished half of the toys in my first speech and language clinic. They had all the toys my husband owned from infancy to his adolescent years. Not only were they happy to pass them along, but they were also excited knowing the items would be used for a good cause.

20. It's Not Working!!!

If all the strategies suggested have been tried without success, and you notice that you and your sugar are still not on the same page, it may be time to seek outside support. Remember: the strategies are meant to be fun and engaging while increasing play and language skills. They are not meant to drive a wedge into your relationship with your child. By chance, if you notice your child is

If you are unsure whether or not your little sugar is meeting speech and language milestones, see Appendix B: Language Milestones, Appendix C: Speech Milestones and Appendix D: Red Flag Behaviors.

responding inconsistently to his or her name, does not respond to familiar directions (i.e., "Come here," "Get bottle," "Want up"), rarely or never imitates words overheard in conversation, has less than ten words by 18 months, and resists play or interaction with you unless he or she wants something, then it is time to have a friendly conversation with your pediatrician.

In the past, the idea to "wait and see" whether or not your child was going to talk was an extremely popular remedy. However, we want to maximize every opportunity for your toddler to acquire new language, understanding language and expanding play skills so that he or she will be ready to participate on the same level as same age peers by kindergarten. So please do not hesitate to reach out to healthcare or other professionals on behalf of your little sugar. You are your child's biggest advocate, and they are relying on you.

21. Are We on Track?

If you went to the gym five times a week for a year, you would use a scale, peer feedback and ultimately how you look and feel to gauge if your exercise routine is on track with the results you would expect. While I understand that parenting is more complex than any workout routine, my point is that you want to know if your child is on track and meeting milestones. Everybody does! I do! There is nothing wrong with desiring to have this information in order to make the necessary adjustments to ensure their optimal success.

Never be afraid to ask care providers about your little sugar's progress. Learning how to ally with your child's educators creates a strong community of adults who are genuinely invested in your little one, observing any changes and tracking their progress.

It also gives you a different perspective on your child's growth and development.

With information readily available online, it is easy to get swept into that rabbit hole. Or maybe you are occasionally comparing your sugar to the other little ones around you. In any case, there is a more concrete way to determine how your little one is doing.

Like at the gym, you expect to make progress and you expect your little one to make progress. That is what you as a parent should be looking for. For example, is my toddler gaining five to seven new words weekly? Are they moving from using single words to two- or three-word phrases and simple four-word sentences? Can I ask them to complete a receptive language task and see that they follow through? While these are common questions I ask my parents, if you are still unsure, here are a few suggestions to help answer your question:

Seek feedback from your child's local daycare or pre-school provider. Rather than asking, "How was my sugar's day?" you can be more specific and ask, "What progress have you noticed with my sugar's language, play and social skills? Are they using their words? Any new words heard?" You might even offer a word bank that is provided in Appendix E. That way, you and the care provider can compare notes.

Ask your pediatrician for a milestone checklist. Most pediatricians are excited about making sure your little one is on track.

Contact a local speech and language pathologist for a consultation. Appendix G: Locating Local Speech-Language Pathologist contains a list of the national American Associations for Speech, Language and Hearing. They provide milestone information from birth though school age. There is also a list of state speech and language associations with local speech pathologists who are more than willing to help.

Conclusion

Sharing my insights, journey and advice about using play to increase language skills and to enhance the relationship with your little one has been so exciting! Small daily changes result in big long-term changes. You have the power to change the trajectory of you and your little one's relationship. Starting early with play will provide the optimal opportunities to build skills that will last a lifetime. Most importantly, you get to be a part of that process and to know that, with intentionality, you sowed a powerful seed that grew throughout your child's life.

As we've said, Rome wasn't built in a day, and building a relationship also takes time and effort. Do not become discouraged if things are not panning out the first time around. Everyone needs time, patience and practice to master the things they love, and what is more important than giving that time to your little one?

So now, you are tasked to go out, make play amazing, have fun, laugh hard, enjoy yourself and make the greatest possible positive impact on the one who loves you most. Challenge yourself to step into amazing play!

Appendix A: Journaling Ideas

Remember, there are no right or wrong ways to journal your thoughts and ideas. If you find yourself stumped when trying to write, here are a few ideas to get the ball rolling. Again, journaling is meant to be reflective about your experience. It can be for your own personal eyes only, or to share with someone you trust who will be supportive.

1. Which goal did I try?
2. Name two or more positive adjectives to describe the experience
3. List two or more things I want to do differently.
4. Exactly what behavior did I want to change?
5. How did my child react when I ... ?
6. How did I react when my child ... ?
7. How will I work to change things in the future?
8. What did I notice differently about my child's behavior?
9. Did I celebrate their success? Did I show them I was proud?
10. Did I celebrate my own success?

Appendix B: Language Milestones

Language milestones are comprised of two parts: receptive and expressive language. The words your child uses when speaking is their expressive language. It is not based on the correct sound production of words, but the use of words. The language your child understands when people speak to them is their receptive language. Listed below are common milestones based on age. It is not uncommon for a child to master milestones in other age ranges. (Check off all that apply.)

12 months to 18 months
___Follows one-step commands
___Attends to pictures
___Responds to "Give me ... "
___Knows four or more body parts on self or others
___Understands 50 or more words
___Gives objects when asked
___Uses single words, points, gestures to communicate
___Says up to 20 words (see Word Bank in Appendix F)
___Says ten words by 18 months (see Word Bank in Appendix F)
___Uses jargon
___Asks for "more"
___Makes two animal sounds
___May imitate words overheard

18 months to 24 months
___Knows six or more body parts
___Understands simple commands, "Stop that," or, "Come here."
___Identifies pictures of common objects when named
___Chooses one object from a group of five upon request
___Understands up to 300 words
___Shakes head yes/no when answering simple questions
___Can identify 12 common objects
___Follows a two-step related command
___Uses 20 to 50 single words (see Word Bank in Appendix F)
___Can produce two-word phrases

___Imitates new words regularly

___Has a sentence-like intonation pattern in jargon

___Asks questions by using a question inflection

___Says first name when asked

24 months to 30 months

___Understands concepts "big" and "little"

___Recognizes family members names

___Understands location phrases

___Follows one- and two-step commands

___Can identify at least one color correctly

___Understands approximately 500 words

___Identifies common actions in pictures

___Uses 50 to 300 words (see Word Bank in Appendix F)

___Understands "one" and "all" concepts

___Knows four common objects by their function (i.e., cup, book, toy)

___May respond with words to simple questions

___Uses two to three words frequently

___Asks for help

___Uses at least one pronoun ("I, me, we, he, she")

30 months to 36 months

___Understands concepts "one" and "all"

___Follows a two-step unrelated command (i.e., "get your shoes and bring your sippy cup")

___Knows parts of an object (i.e., car-wheels, door, window, radio)

___Answers to some "wh" questions

___Understands at least five action words

___Understands 900 or more words

___Uses 200 or more words (see word bank in Appendix F)

___May "stutter" on words, especially when excited

___Uses plurals and prepositions

___Tells gender (boy or girl)

___Sentence length is between two and four words

___Expresses physical state ("I am hungry.")

___Counts to three

___Enjoys talking to other children

36 months to 48 months

___Understands 1,200 or more words

___Understands time concepts (morning, lunch, dinner, tonight)

___Able to follow a simple plot in a children's book

___Follows positional commands ("Push the chair under the table.")

___Understands and participates in short conversations

___Identifies colors and common shapes

___Uses 900 to 1500 words

___Is able to tell a short story

___Sentence length is between four and five words

___States first and last name when asked

___Asks many questions

___Uses plurals consistently

___Initiates conversations and comments

Appendix C: Speech Milestones

Speech milestones are based on the sounds your child produces. Below is a list of sounds that your child should master within each age range. It is not uncommon if your child masters sounds within other age ranges. It is also common for your child to use sounds in one part of the word and maybe not the other (i.e., "pot" versus "hah" for hop).

12 months to 18 months
Consonants m, p, b, n, h, t, d, w, and y are heard

18 months to 24 months
Masters vowels

24 months to 30 months
70% of child's words are understood

30 months to 36 months
75% to 90% of child's words are understood

36 months to 48 months
100% of child's words are understood

Appendix D: Red Flag Behaviors

These flags that could signal autism are adapted from the U.S. Centers for Disease Control (CDC) and available at
https://www.cdc.gov/ncbddd/autism/signs.html
Consult your pediatrician or other healthcare professional for follow up.

- Not responding to their name by 12 months of age
- Not pointing at objects to show interest (i.e., pointing at an airplane flying over) by 14 months
- Not playing "pretend" games (i.e., pretending to "feed" a doll) by 18 months
- Avoiding eye contact and wanting to be alone
- Having trouble understanding other people's feelings or talking about their own feelings
- Having delayed speech and language skills
- Repeating words or phrases over and over (i.e., echolalia)
- Giving unrelated answers to questions
- Getting upset by minor changes
- Having obsessive interests
- Flapping their hands, rocking their body or spinning in circles
- Having unusual reactions to the way things sound, smell, taste, look or feel

Appendix E: First Word Bank

Directions: Circle all words your child currently uses to communicate verbally. Please include words your child uses without repeating. Please include words your child uses to communicate with others to label, call attention, request, negate, or begin/reply to conversational turns.

Child's current age (in months)_____

Pre-language Sounds

- ☐ Coos
- ☐ Ooh
- ☐ Ahh
- ☐ Ohh
- ☐ Eee

Sounds not listed:

- ☐ _____
- ☐ _____
- ☐ _____
- ☐ _____
- ☐ _____

Babbles

- ☐ Ba-ba
- ☐ Ma-ma
- ☐ Da-da
- ☐ Ta-ta
- ☐ Pa-pa
- ☐ Wa-wa
- ☐ Ka-ka

Sounds not listed:

- ☐ _____
- ☐ _____
- ☐ _____
- ☐ _____

Animals

- ☐ Bear
- ☐ Bird
- ☐ Bunny
- ☐ Cat
- ☐ Chicken
- ☐ Cow
- ☐ Dog
- ☐ Duck
- ☐ Elephant
- ☐ Fish
- ☐ Frog
- ☐ Horse
- ☐ Lizard
- ☐ Lion
- ☐ Monkey
- ☐ Piggy
- ☐ Puppy
- ☐ Snake
- ☐ Tiger
- ☐ Turkey
- ☐ Turtle

Food

Drinks

- Apple Juice
- Juice
- Milk
- Orange Juice
- Soda
- Tea
- Water

Fruits

- Apple
- Banana
- Watermelon
- Grapes
- Pear
- Mango
- Plum
- Melon
- Orange

Breakfast

- Bread
- Toast
- Cereal
- Egg
- Pancake
- Toast
- Waffle

Lunch/Dinner

- Broccoli
- Carrot
- Chicken
- Chicken Nugget
- Hamburger
- Hotdog
- Macaroni
- Meat
- Pasta
- Pizza
- Sandwich
- Soup
- Spaghetti
- Spinach
- Tofu

Snacks/Other

- Candy
- Cheese
- Chips
- Crackers
- Fruit cup
- Fruit snack
- Granola Bar
- Lunchables
- Popcorn
- Pretzel
- Rice cakes
- Seaweed
- Trail mix
- Cookie
- Ice Cream

Toys

- Baby
- Ball
- Balloon
- Bear
- Blocks
- Book
- Bubbles
- Car
- Chalk
- Crayons
- Doll
- Playdough
- Potato Head
- Puzzle
- Wind-up toy

People

- Aunt
- Baby
- Boy
- Dada
- Doctor
- Favorite Character
- Friends Name
- Girl
- Grandma
- Grandpa
- Lady
- Mama
- Own Name
- Pet Name
- Uncle

Outdoors

- Flower
- House
- Leaf
- Moon
- Park
- Playhouse
- Rain
- Sidewalk
- Slide
- Snow
- Star
- Street
- Swing
- Sun
- Tree

Bugs

- Ant
- Bee
- Bug
- Butterfly
- Slug
- Spider

Body Part

- Arm
- Belly
- Bottom
- Chin
- Ear
- Elbow
- Eyes
- Face
- Finger
- Foot
- Hair
- Hand
- Knee
- Leg
- Mouth
- Neck
- Nose
- Teeth
- Thumb
- Toe
- Tummy

Clothes

- Boots
- Coat
- Diaper
- Dress
- Flip Flops
- Gloves
- Hat
- Jacket
- Mittens
- PJs
- Pull Up
- Pants
- Rain Boots
- Sandals
- Shirt
- Shoes
- Shorts
- Slippers
- Socks
- Sweater
- Vest

Hygiene

- Blow nose
- Brush
- Comb
- Glasses
- Tissue
- Toothbrush
- Toothpaste
- Wash face
- Wash hands

House Items

- Bathtub
- Bed
- Blanket
- Bottle
- Bowl
- Chair
- Crib
- Cup
- Door
- Floor
- Fork
- Glass
- iPad
- iPhone
- Key
- Knife
- Light
- Mirror
- Money
- Paper
- Pen
- Phone
- Pillow
- Plate
- Potty
- Radio
- Room
- Sink
- Soap
- Sofa
- Spoon
- Stairs
- Table
- Towel
- Trash
- TV
- Umbrella
- Watch
- Window

Places

- Chick-Fil-A
- Church
- Home
- Hospital
- Library
- McDonald's
- Park
- School
- Store
- Zoo

Action

- Away
- Bath
- Bring
- Catch
- Clap
- Close
- Come
- Cough
- Cut
- Dance
- Eat Dinner
- Feed
- Finish
- Fix

- Get
- Give
- Go
- Have
- Help
- Hide
- Hit
- Hop
- Hug
- Jump
- Kick
- Kiss
- Knock
- Look

- Love
- Make
- Naptime
- Ni-night
- Outside
- Peek-a-boo
- Pee pee
- Potty
- Push
- Read
- Ride
- Run
- See
- Show

- Sing
- Sit
- Sleep
- Stop
- Take
- Throw
- Tickles
- Walk
- Want
- Wash
- Wash hands
- Wash face
- Wash nose

Vehicles

- Airplane
- Bike
- Boat
- Bus
- Car

- Dump Truck
- Helicopter
- Moped
- Motorcycle
- Pick-up Truck

- Plane
- Scooter
- Skateboard
- Skates
- Stroller

- Subway Train
- Train
- Trolley
- Truck
- Wagon

Describing Words

- Bad
- Big
- Broken
- Clean
- Cold
- Dark
- Done
- Dirty

- Down
- Gone
- Good
- Happy
- Heavy
- Hot
- Hungry
- Little

- Mine
- More
- Open
- Pretty
- Right
- Shut
- Stinky
- That

- This
- Those
- Tired
- Under
- Up
- Wet
- Yucky

Colors

- Black
- Blue
- Green
- Orange
- Pink
- Purple
- Red
- White
- Yellow

Sounds

- Growl
- Meow
- Roar
- Shhhh...
- Woof woof

Songs

- A, B, C...
- 1, 2, 3...
- Baby Shark
- Elmo Song
- Five Little Monkeys
- One, Two, Buckle My Shoe
- Patty Cake, Patty Cake
- Ring Around the Roses
- This Little Finger
- This Old Man

Early Conversational Words

- Boo boo
- Bye bye
- Curse words
- Here
- Hello
- Hi
- In
- Me
- Mine
- No
- Off
- On
- Out
- Please
- Thank You
- There
- Welcome
- What
- Where
- Why
- Yes
- You
- Yum

Age Range	Typical Expressive Language Milestones	Atypical Expressive Language Milestones
16 months to 18 months	5 words to 10 words	16 months = 4 words or less 18 months = 8 words or less
18 months to 24 months	10 words to 50 words	18 months = 8 words or less 24 months = 40 words or less
24 months to 30 months	50 words to 300 words	24 months = 40 words or less 30 months = 240 words or less
30 months to 36 months	200 words to 900 words	30 months = 240 words or less 36 months = 720 words or less

Appendix F: Toy Suppliers

This is a list of the current toy lending libraries in the United States of America (adapted from usatla.org).

ARIZONA

Arizona Technology Access Program
Submit state form found at www.adeatloan.org
Adaptive toys and equipment sent to schools short-term
Special Needs
877-523-6759
www.adeatloan.org

Avondale Civic Center Library
11350 W. Civic Center Drive
Avondale 85323
STEM items, sports equipment
General Public
623-333-2602
www.avondalelibrary.org

San Garcia Western Ave. Library
495 E. Western Avenue
STEM items, sports equipment
General Public
Avondale 85323
623-333-2601
www.avondalelibrary.org

Northern Arizona University, Meyerson
Toy Kits
Rm 171 Human Development, Riordan Road
Flagstaff 86011
Adaptive toys/materials
Special Needs, General Public
877-502-3045
http://nau,edu

Payson Public Library
328 N. McLane Road
Payson 85541
Puzzles, puppets
General Public
928-474-9260
www.paysonaz.gov

ADAPT Shop
2850 North 24th Street
Phoenix 85008
Toys/Adaptives
Special Needs
602-266-5976
www.swhd.org/adapt/adapt

Tiny Tree Library
Broadmoor-Broadway Village
Corner E. Arroyo Chico & Malvern St.
Tucson 85716
Toys/books
General Public
Tiny corner library in neighborhood

MCSA R&R Child Development Center
Martin Avenue, Bldg. 1071
Yuma 85369
Toys, books, equipment
Military Families
928-269-3251
www.militaryinstallations

CALIFORNIA

Modoc Child Care Resource and
Referral
112 E. 2nd Street
Alturas 96101
Books/Toys/Videos/Mobile
530-233-5437

EC Education Toy & Resource Library
365 Nevada Street
Auburn 95603
Materials/Books/Resources
Families/Providers
530-745-1380
www.placercoe.k12.ca.us

Community Connection Resource
Library
2000 24th Street
Bakersfield 93301
Toys/Books
Child Care Providers
661-861-5200
www.kernchildcare.org

Habitot
1563 Solano Avenue
Berkeley 94707
Toys/Training
General Public
510-647-1111
habitot@lmi.net
www.habitot.org

Resource Center
2547 Eighth Street, #12A
Berkeley 94710
Toys/Adaptives/Electronics/Training
Special Needs
510-841-3224
info@cforat.org
www.cforat.org

R&R Child Care Connection Resource
Library
164 Grandview Drive
Bishop 93514
Toys/Books/Materials
General Public
760-873-5123 ext. 0

Child Care Resource Library
20001 Prairie Street
Chatsworth 91311
Toys/Books
General Public
818-717-1000
www.ccrcla.org

Valley Oak Children's Resource Library
287 Rio Lindo Avenue
Chico 95926
Books, toys, training
Childcare providers/parents
530-895-3572
www.valleyoakchildren.org

MAO Toy Lending Library
972 S. Goodrich Blvd.
Commerce 90022
Books/Toys/Videos/Equipment
Providers/families
323-890-1555
www.maof.org

Del Norte Co. R&R Toy Room
212 K Street
Crescent City 95531
Toys/Books/Play area
Parents
707-464-8311
www.dnccc.com

City of Davis Toy Lending Closet
23 Russell Blvd.
Davis 95161
Books/Toys/Adaptives/Training
General Public
530-757-5695
800-723-3001
www.cityofdavis.org/pcs/childcare

El Segundo Kiwanis Club Toy Loan
111 W. Mariposa Avenue
El Segundo 90245
Books/Toys/Adaptives
General Public
310-524-2722

SFCS Lending Library
421 Executive Court North
Fairfield, 94534
Curriculum Kits/Materials
General Public
707-863-3950
info@solanofamily.org
www.solanofamily.org

CSN Resource & Toy Library
1911 N. Helm Avenue
Fresno 93727
Toys/Books/Mobile
Childcare Providers
559-456-8195
info@cvcsn.org
www.cvcsn.org

Asian Service Center Toy Loan
14112 S Kingsley Drive
Gardena 90249
Toys/Books
General Public
310-217-7300

SNCS Resource Library
256 Buena Vista Street, Suite 110
Grass Valley 95945
Toys/Materials/Books/DVDs
General Public
530-272-8866
Grassvalley@sncs.org
www.sncs.org

Kings Community Action
R&R Toy Lending Library
1130 N. 11th Avenue
Hanford 93230
Toys/Books
Child Care Providers
559-582-4386
www.kcao.org

Go Kids Resource Room
1101 Community Parkway
Hollister 95023
Theme/Curriculum Kits
Child Care Providers
831-637-9205 ext. 0
www.gokids.org

Lend & Learn Toys
142 Burke Lane
Kneeland 95549
707-834-3168

Children's Society Lending Library
330 Golden Shore, Suite 20
Long Beach 90802
Toys/Books/Videos
General Public
562-256-7490
www.chs-ca.org

Toy and Resource Library
3311 Pacific Avenue
Livermore 94550
Books/Toys
General Public
925-249-3923
mail@childcarelinks.org
www.childcarelinks.org

Toy Loan & Volunteer Services Section
LA County Dept. of Public Social
Services
2615 S. Grand Avenue, 2nd Floor
Los Angeles 90007
213-744-4347
toyloan@dpsslacounty.gov
dpss.lacounty.gov/wps/portal/dpss/main/
programs-and-services/toy-loan/

Koch-Young Resource Center
Frank D. Lanterman Regional Center
3303 Wilshire Blvd., Suite 700
Los Angeles 90010
Serves children and adults with
developmental disabilities. Provides
family support, education,
training, assistive technology and
lending library
213-252-5600
www.lanterman.org

Crystal Stairs Resource Library
5110 Goldleaf Cir., Suite 150, Room 301
Los Angeles 90056
Toys/Materials
Child Care Providers
323-421-1210
www.crystalstaiars.org

SNCS Resource Library
105 Beckwith Street
Loyalton 96118
Toys/Materials/Books/DVDs
General Public
530-993-1288
www.sncs.org

MCCAA Resource & Referral Child Care
1225 Gill Avenue
Madera 93637
Books/Toys/Training
Child Care Providers
559-675-5751
800-505-0404
resources@madnet.net
www.maderacap.org

ICES Resource & Referral Lending
Library
5067 Jones Street
Mariposa 95338
Books/Videos/Training
Child Care Providers
209-966-4474
www.mariposa-lpc.org/links.html

Alpine Choices for Children Lending
Library
100 Foothill Road, Suite D-6
Markleeville 96120
Toys/Books
Childcare providers, parents
530-694-1889
www.choices4children-alpine.org

CCR&R Stanislaus Toy Library
917 Oakdale Road
Modesto 95355
Toys/Games/Kits
General Public
209-238-6400
www.stancoe.org

Project Playroom
1900 Garden Road, Suite 210
Monterey 93940
Therapeutic Toys for Special Needs
Children
831-229-2433
info@projectplayroom.org
www.projectplayroom.org

Community Resources For Children Toy
Library
3299 Claremont Way, Suite 1
Napa 94558
Toys/Materials/Kits
General Public
707-253-0376 ext. 200
info@crcnapa.org
www.crcnapa.org

Katie's Korner Adaptive Toy Lending
Library
At Nipomo Recreation Comm. Room
671 W. Tefft Street, Suite 2
Nipomo 93444
Adaptive Toys/Special Needs
805-547-1914
www.jackshelpinghand.ocm

CHS R&R Toy & Resource Library
333 South Anita Dr. Suite 305
Orange 92868
Toys/Materials
General Public
714-543-2273
www.chs-ca.org

R&R Resource Library
676 E. Walker Street
Orland 95963
Books/Toys/Videos
General Public
530-865-1118
800-394-2818
www.glencoe.org

Ventura County Resource & Toy Library
221 E. Ventura Blvd., Bldg. 211
Oxnard 93036
Activity materials/Audio/Visuals
Family Child Care Providers/ EC
Students
805-485-7878 x512
800-962-5437
www.cdrv.org

Child Care Resource Center
250 Grand Cypress Avenue
Palmdale 93551
Toys/Books
General public
661-789-1200
www.ccrcla.org

CCIS Provider Library
2465 E. Walnut Street
Pasadena 91107
Books/Toys/Videos
Childcare Providers
626-449-8221
Lacey Olivarez
www.ccispasadena.org

Pico Park Community Center Toy Loan
9528 Beverly Blvd.
Pico Rivera 90601
Toys
General Public
562-801-4470

Toy & Resource Library
6601 Owens Dr. Suite 100
Pleasanton 94588
Books/Toys/Training
General Public
925-417-8733
mail@childcarelinks.org
www.childcarelinks.org

Bill Ewing Provider Resource Center
1460 E. Holt Avenue, Suite 130
Pomona 91767
Toys/Books/Videos
Teachers/Centers/ Family Care Providers
909-397-4740 x5289
909-397-4740 ext. 6030
www.pusd.org

R&R Toy and Resource Library
536 Jackson Street
Quincy 95971
Books/Toys/Adaptives/Training
General Public
530-283-4453
ccrr@plumasruralservices.org
www.plumasruralservices.org

Tehama Co. R&R Toy Lending Library
645 Antelope Blvd., #34
Red Bluff 96080
Toys/Kits/Resources
General Public
530-529-3131
www.shastacoe.org

Southern Humboldt Family Resource
Center
Toy Lending Library
344 Humboldt Ave. PO Box 369
Redway 95660
Toys
General Public
707-923-1147
www.humboldt.k12.ca.us/sohumb_usd/
redway/

Child Action Resource Library
9800 Old Winery Place
Sacramento 95827
Theme boxes/Curriculum Kits/Adaptive
Devices
General Public
916-369-0191
www.childaction.org

UCP of Greater Sacramento
4350 Auburn Blvd.
Sacramento 95841
Toys/Adaptives for Children with Special
Needs
916-565-7700
ucp@ucpsacto.org
www.ucpsacto.org

John Steinbeck Library
350 Lincoln Avenue
Salinas 93901
The Toy Lending Collection includes
educational, imaginative and active-
play toys, puzzles and games
General Public
831-758-7311
www.salinaspubliclibrary.org/john-
steinbeck-library

Calaveras C. R&R Resource Library
501 F Gold Strike Road
San Andreas 95249
Books/Toys/Educational Videos
General Public
209-754-1075
www.theresourceconnection.net

Resource & Referral Toy Library
1111 East Mill Street, Suite 100
San Bernardino 92408
Toys/Books/Materials
Family Childcare Providers
909-384-1492
800-722-1091
www.kidscare.com

UCP Toy & Software Lending Library
6162 Mission Gorge Rd. Suite F
San Diego 92120
Toys/Books/Adaptives/Electronics
Mobile for toy delivery
Children with Special Needs
858-278-5420
www.ucpsdtechcenter.org

Children's Council Lending Library
445 Church Street
San Francisco 94114
Toys/Books/Materials
Childcare providers and parents
415-343-3300/415-343-3309
www.childrenscouncil.org

PTRAC Resource Center
1197 Lick Avenue
San Jose 95110
Toys/Books/Materials
Child Care Providers
408-295-0650
www.choices4children-santaclara.org

Community Action Toy & Resource
Library
1030 Southwood Drive
San Luis Obispo 93401
Toys/Equipment/Materials
General Public
805-541-2272
888-727-2272
www.capslo.org

Jack's Adaptive Toy Lending Library
At Central Coast Gymnastics
21 Zaca Lane, #100
San Luis Obispo 93410
Adaptive Toys
Special Needs
805-547-1914
www.jackshelpinghand.com

SBFC Child Development Lending
Library
1124 Castillo Street
Santa Barbara 93101
Books/Toys/Adaptives/Training
General Public
805-962-8988
www.sbfcc.org

SBFC Child Development Lending
Library
705 E. Main Street, Suite 106
Santa Maria 93454
Books/Toys/Adaptives/Training
General Public
805-925-7071
www.sbfc.org

Community Child Care Council
Resource Library
131A Stony Circle, Suite 300
Santa Rosa 95401
Toys/Books/Curriculum Kits
Child Care Providers/ Enrolled Families
707-522-1413 x126
www.sonoma4Cs.org

Infant/Child Enrichment Services
Lending Library
20993 Niagara River Drive
Sonora 95370
Curriculum Boxes/Books/Videos/
Training
Child Care Providers
209-533-0377
info@icesagency.org
www.icesagency.org

Resource Lending Library
1029 Takela Drive, Suite 1
South Lake Tahoe 96150
Books/Toys/Adaptives/Mobile
Child Care Providers/Parents
530-541-5848, ext. 110
www.choices4children-eldorado.org

Resource Lending Library
509 W. Weber Avenue, Ste. 104
Stockton 95203
Toys/Activity Kits/Books
General Public
209-461-2908
childcare@frrcsj.org
www.frrcsj.org

Family Resource Library
5151 Pacific Avenue
Stockton 95207
Books/Toys/Training/Mobile
College Community
209-954-5700
www.deltacollege.edu/dept/childdevctr

Lassen Child & Family Resource Library
336 Alexander Avenue
Susanville 96130
Toys/Books/Videos
General Public
530-257-9781
www.lassencfr.com

Amador Co. R&R Resource Library
10877 Conductor Blvd.
Sutter Creek 95685
Toys, books, educational videos
Childcare providers, parents
209-223-1624
www.theresourceconnection.net

Tracy Resource Center
324 E. 11th Street
Tracy 95376
Books/Toys/Training
Childcare providers/Parents
209-461-2908
800-526-1555
childcare@frrcsj.org
www.frrcsj.org

SNCS Resource Library
10075 Lavon Avenue, Suite 201A
Truckee 96161
Toys/Materials/Books/DVDs
General Public
530-587-5960
truckee@sncs.org
www.sncs.org

Rural Community Toy & Resource
Library
413 N. State Street
Ukiah 95482
Toys/Books/Adaptives
General Public
707-467-3200
800-606-5550
www.ncoinc.org

Resource & Referral Toy Library
16519 Victor Street, Suite 427
Victorville 92395
Toys/Books/Materials
Families, Child Care Providers
760-245-0770 x207
800-722-1091
www.kidscare.com

Tulare County Resource & Referral
Service
7000 Doe Avenue, Suite C
Visalia 93291
Books/Toys/Adaptives/Training
Child Care Providers
559-651-0862
800-613-6262
www.tcoe.org

Lending Library - ROVE
111 Mountainview Street
Weaverville 96093
Toys/Books/Materials/Training
General Public
530-623-2024
800-358-5251
www.humanresponsenetwork.org

West Sacramento Toy Library
Arthur F. Turner Community Library
1212 Merkley Avenue
West Sacramento 95691
Toys/Books
General Public
916-375-6465
WestSacLibrary@yolocounty.org
www.yolocounty.org

Adventure Park Toy Loan Center
10130 South Gunn Avenue
Whittier 90605
Toys/Materials
General Public
562-698-7645

Amigo County Park Toy Loan Center
5700 S. Juarez Avenue
Whittier 90606
Toys/Materials
General Public
562-908-4702

Woodland Toy Library
1017 Main Street
Woodland 95695
Toys
County Residents
530-669-7139 Carol Barnett
woodlandtoylibrary@gmail.com
www.cityofwoodland.org

Education & Resource Library
1650 Sierra Avenue, Suite 102
Yuba City 95993
Books/Toys/Adaptives/Training
General Public
530-673-7503
www.chs-ca.org/

COLORADO

Northwest Denver Toy Library-Smiley
Branch
4501 W. 46th Avenue
Denver 80212
Toys/Games/Puzzles/Costumes
General Public
720-865-0260
toylibrarydenver@aol.com
www.denvertoylibrary.com

Play & Learn Library-Denver Options
9900 East Iliff Avenue
Denver 80231
Adaptive Toys/Equipment Therapists
330-636-5600
info@denveroptions.org
www.denveroptions.org

Star Point Family Resource Center-
Freemont County
1333 Elm Avenue
Cannon City 81212
Mobile Unit goes to homes
Toys/Materials
Enrolled Early Head Start Families
719-275-0550
www.starpointco.com

Clear Creek Resource Center
1531 Colorado Blvd. Toys
Idaho Springs 80452
General Public
303-478-1795
www.co.clear-creek.co.us

Red Feather Lakes Community Library
Toy Lending Library
71 Firehouse Lane
Red Feather Lakes 80548
Toys/Books
General Public
970-881-2664
www.redfeather.colibraries.org

CONNECTICUT

Bethlehem Public Library
32 Main Street South
Bethlehem 06751
Books/Toys/Games
General Public
203-266-7792
www.bethlehemlibraryct.org

Bristol Public Library
5 High Street
Bristol 06010
Books/Toys/Games
General Public
860-584-7787
www.bristollib.com

Durham Public Library
7 Maple Street
Durham 06422
Books/Toys/Games
General Public
860-349-9544
www.durhamlibrary.org

Mansfield Public Library
54 Warrensville Road
Mansfield 06250
Books/Toys/Kits
General Public
860-423-2501
mansfield@biblio.org
www.mansfieldpubliclibraryct.org

East Lyme Public Library
39 Society Road
Niantic 06357
Books/Toys/Kits
General Public
860-739-6026
elpl@ely.lioninc.org
www.ely.lioninc.org

Tech Tot Library UCP Eastern CT
42 Norwich Road
Quaker Hill 06375
Toys/Adaptives/Equipment
Special Needs
860-443-3800 ext. 11
www.ucpect.org

Southbury Public Library
100 Poverty Road
Southbury 06488
Puzzles/Books
General Public
203-262-0626
www.southburylibrary.org
Terryville Public Library
238 Main Street
Terryville 06786
Books/Toys/Games/Puzzles
General Public
860-582-3121
publiclibrary@plymouthct.us
www.terryvillepl.info

Toy Lending Library
95 Merritt Blvd.
Trumbull 06611
Books/Toys/Adaptives/Training
General Public
203-386-2743
www.stvincentsspecialneeds.org

Willimantic Public Library
905 Main Street
Willimantic 06226
Puzzles/Books
General Public
860-465-3082
www.willimanticlibrary.org

Westport Public Library
20 Jessup Road
Westport 06880
Books/Kits
General Public
203-291-4800
kids@westportlibrary.orgwww.
westportlibrary.org

GEORGIA

Lekotek of Georgia, Inc.
1955 Cliff Valley Way, Suite 102
Atlanta 30329
Books/Toys/Adaptives/Electronics/
Training/Mobile
Special Needs
404-633-3430
www.lekotekga.org

Lekotek of Georgia - CHOA-Gwinnett
2660 Satellite Blvd.
Duluth 30096
Books/Toys/Adaptives/Training
Special Needs
404-785-8423
www.lekotekga.org

Lekotek of Georgia-Southside Satellite
118 Governor's Square Pkwy, Suite B
Fayetteville 30215
Books/Toys/Adaptives/Training
Special Needs
707-289-3276
www.lekotekga.org

Lekotek of Georgia-Gainesville Satellite
3485 McEver Road Gainesville 30504
Books/Toys/Adaptives/Training
Special Needs
706-506-2835
www.lekotekga.org

Lekotek of Georgia - Cobb Satellite
1925 Vaughn Rd. N.W., Suite 150
Kennesaw 30144
Books/Toys/Adaptives/Training
770-420-9889
www.lekotekga.org

Lekotek of Georgia - Alpharetta
11835 Alpharetta Hwy.
Roswell 30076
Books/Toys/Adaptives/Training
Special Needs
404-785-8525

Roswell Lekotek of Georgia - Alpharetta
11835 Alpharetta Hwy.
Books/Toys/Adaptives/Training
Special Needs
404-785-8525

HAWAII

Assistive Technology Centers of Hawaii
200 N. Vineyard Blvd., Suite 430
Honolulu 96817
Adaptive Toys/Materials
Special Needs
808-532-7110
www.atrc.org

MICHIGAN

Arcadia Branch Library
3586 Glovers Lake Rd.
Arcadia 49613
Toys/Kits
General Public
231-889-4230
www.manisteelibrary.org

Keddie Norconk Memorial Library
12325 Virginia Street
Bear Lake 49614
Toys/Kits
General Public
231-864-2700
www.manisteelibrary.org

Baldwin Public Library
300 West Merrill St.
Birmingham 48009
Toys/Games
General Public
248-647-1700
www.baldwinlib.org

Bloomfield Township Public Library
1099 Lone Pine Rd.
Bloomfield Township 48302
Toys/Adaptive Toys
General Public, Special Needs
248-642-5800
www.btpl.org

Charlevoix Public Library
220 West Clinton St.
Charlevoix 49720
Toys/Puzzles/Games
General Public
231-547-2651
www.charlevoixlibrary.org

disAbility Connect PERC
409 Linden Ave.
Jackson 49203
Adaptive Toys
Special Needs
517-782-6054
www.disabilityconnect.org

Keleva Branch Library
14618 Walta St.
Keleva 49645
Toys/Kits
General Public
231-362-3178
www.manisteelibrary.org

Manistee County Library
95 Maple St.
Manistee 49660
Toys/Kits
General Public
231-723-2519
www.manisteelibrary.org

Niles District Library, Miss Diane's Toys
620 E. Main St.
Niles 49120
Toys/Games/Puppets
General Public
269-683-8545
info@nileslibrary.net
www.nileslibrary.com

Onekama Branch Library
5283 Main St.
Onekama 49675
Toys/Kits
General Public
232-889-4041
www.manisteelibrary.org

ARC Lekotek
26049 Five Mile Rd.
Redford 48239
Toys/Adaptives
Special Needs
313-532-8524
www.thearcnw.org

Welston Branch Library
1273 Seaman Rd.
Welston 49689
Toys/Kits
General Public
231-848-4013
www.manisteelibrary.org

Ypsilanti Library Whittaker Branch
577 Whittaker Rd.
Ypsilanti 48197
Play Kits
General Public
734-482-4110
www.ypsilantiibrary.org/

Ypsilanti Library Michigan Branch
229 W. Michigan Ave.
Ypsilanti 48197
Play Kits
General Public
734-482-4110
www.ypsilantiibrary.org/

Ypsilanti Library Superior Branch
8795 MacArthur Blvd.
Ypsilanti 48198
Play Kits
General Public
734-482-4110
www.ypsilantiibrary.org/

MINNESOTA

Belle Plaine Public Library
125 West Main Street
Belle Plaine 56011
General Public
952-873-6767
www.scott.lib.mn.us

Little Giants Early Learning Center
Blue Earth Ag Center
425 South Grove Street
Blue Earth 56013
Toys/Resources
Families
507-525-5554
http://www.blueearth.k12.mn.us/

Brainerd Public Library
416 South 5th Street
Brainerd 56401
Kits for Kids
Child Care Providers
218-829-5574
www.brainerd.com/library

Buhl Public Library
400 Jones Avenue, PO Box 664
Buhl 55713
218-258-3391
www.buhl.lib.mn.us

Cloquet Public Library
320 14th Street
Cloquet 55720
Books/ Videos/Toys
General Public
218-879-1531
Cloquet.library@gmail.com
www.cloquet.lib.mn.us

Detroit Lakes Public Library
1000 Washington Avenue
Detroit Lakes 56501
Toys/Books
General Public
218-847-2168
Detroit@larl.org
www.larl.org/detroit_lakes

Duluth Public Library
520 W. Superior
Duluth 55082
Books/Toys
General Public
218-730-4200 opt. 4
webmail@duluth.lib.mn.
www.duluth.lib.mn.us

Grand Marais Public Library
104 2nd Avenue West
Grand Marais 55604
Toys/Books/Videos
General Public
218-387-1140
gmlib@arrowhead.lib.mn.us
www.grandmariaslibrary.org

Hibbing Public Library - Toy Library
2020 E. 5th Avenue
Hibbing 55746
Toys/Learning Kits
Licensed Child Care Providers
218-362-5959
hibbingpl@arrowhead.lib.mn.us
www.hibbing.lib.mn.us

Minneapolis Toy Library (within
Richfield Lutheran Church)
8 W 60th Street
Minneapolis, 55419
Toy Rental
General Public
651-324-3589
mplstoylibrary.org

Owatonna Public Library-Toy Library
105 N. Elm Avenue
Owatonna 55060
Books/Toys
General Public
507-444-2460
info@watonna.lib.mn.us
www.owatonna.lib.mn.us

Pine River Public Library
212 Park Avenue, PO Box 14
Pine River 56474
Toys/Puppets
General Public
218-587-4639
pineriver@krls.org
www.krls.org/branches/branch_pr.html

Covill Family Center Toy Lending Library
269 E. Fifth Street
Red Wing 55066
Toys/Resources
General Public
651-385-8000
www.redwing.k12.mn.us/school348

Rochester Public Library
101 2nd Street SE
Rochester 55904
Story Time Kits
General Public
507-328-2309
www.rochesterpubliclibrary.org

ECFE Parent Resource Library
Parkview Center School
701 County Road, B West
Roseville 55113
Toys/Books/Parenting Books
General Public
651-487-4361
info@isd623
www.isd623.org

Child Care Choices
640 54th Avenue, Suite A
Saint Cloud 56303
Books/Toys/Training
Child Care Providers
320-251-5081
800-288-8549
ccci@childcarechoices.net
www.childcarechoices.net

Scott & Carver County Office
Community Action
712 Canterbury Road
Shakopee 55379
Learning Kits/Equipment
Child Care Providers
952-496-2125
info@capagency.org
www.capagency.org

Silver Bay Elementary School, Room 104
ECFE Lending Library-Parent-Child
135 Banks Blvd.
Silver Bay, 55614
Toys/Activity Kits/Books/Videos
Families
218-226-4437 x8158
www.isd381.k12.mn.us

Two Harbors Community Education
ECFE Lending Library
16640 Hwy. 2, Suite 1640
Two Harbors 55616
Toys/Activity Kits/Books/Videos
218-834-8201 x8230
www.isd381.k12.mn.us

MISSISSIPPI

Biloxi Family Resource Center
140 St. John Street, Lopez School
Campus
Biloxi 39530
Toys/Games/Books
General Public
228-297-6808
www.excelby5.com

Cleveland Parent & Teacher Resource
Center
305 Sunflower Rd. (Hwy 8 West)
Cleveland 38732
Toys/Books/Games
General Public
662-846-1297
www.excelby5.com

The Children's Center
JB George Bldg., #109
118 College Dr. #5092
Hattiesburg 39406
Adaptive Toys/Equipment
Special Needs Families, Therapists
601 266-5222
www.usm.edu/children's center

First Regional Library EC Resource
Center
370 West Commerce Street
Hernando 38632
Toys/Books/Kits
Families, Child Care Providers
662-429-4439 x 101
www.firstregional.org

Mid-Jackson Family Resource Center
301 Adelle Street
Jackson 39202
Toys/Books/Games
General Public
601-354-7770
www.excelby5.com

Toy Library & Tech Center
USM Institute For Disability Studies
730 E. Beach Blvd.
Long Beach 39560
Adaptive Toys/Equipment/Training
Special Needs Families, Educators
228-214-3400
www.usm.edu/gulfcoast/ids

Family Education Center
Moss Point Schools
3524 Prentiss Avenue
Moss Point 39563
Toys/Books/Games
General Public
228-475-7101
www.excelby5.com

LOU Excel by 5 Family Resource Center
1097 Jackson Avenue West
Oxford 38655
Toys/Books/Games
General Public
662-915-2704
www.excelby5.com

Early Beginnings Resource Library
Excel by 5
Market Street (Across from the High
School)
Pascagoula 39567
Toys/Books/Games
General Public
228-938-6418
www.excelby5.com

Parent Center
Excel by 5
328 Fourth Street
Wiggins 39577
Toys/Books/Games
General Public
601 528-9098
www.excelby5.com

MISSOURI

Play Power c/o Easter Seals
13975 Manchester Road, #2
Ballwin 63011
Books/Toys/Adaptives/Training
Special Needs, Birth to Five
636-227-6030
www.mo.easter-seals.org

Success by 6 Belton School District
Grace Early Childhood Center
614 W. Mill Street
Belton 64012
Toys/Books
General Public
816-348-1029
www.bornlearningkc.org

Success by 6
Family Literacy Center/McCarter Center
5000 Valley View Road
Blue Springs 64015
Toys/Books
General Public
816-228-8816
www.bornlearningkc.org

Success by 6
Parents as Teachers/Consiglio
Education Center
1501 NW Jefferson Street
Blue Springs 64015
Toys/Books
General Public
816-308-6540
www.bornlearningkc.org

Lend and Learn North
1023 East Highway 22
Centralia 65240
Books/Toys/ Parent Education

Lend and Learn
1010 Fay Street
Columbia 65201
Books/Toys/Parent Education
General Public
573-777-1815

Parents as Teachers Toy Lending Room
Columbia Public Schools
2191 Smiley Lane
Columbia 65202
Toys/Puzzles
General Public
573-214-3955

Daniel Boone Regional Library
Many locations through Book Mobile
100 W. Broadway
Columbia 65203
Toys/Books/Kits/ Story Boxes/Parenting
Kits
General Public
573-443-3161
www.dbrl.org

Success by 6
High Grove Early Childhood Center
2500 High Grove Road
Grandview 64030
Toys/Books
General Public
816-316-5489
www.bornlearningkc.org

Success by 6
Harrisonville Early Childhood Center
500 Polar Lane
Harrisonville 64701
Toys/Books
General Public
816-380-4421
www.bornlearningkc.org

Success by 6
Hanthorn Early Education
1511 S. Kings Highway
Independence 64055
Toys/Books
General Public
816-521-5485
www.bornlearningkc.org

Success by 6
Indian Trail Elem. School
24300 E. Bundschu Road
Independence 64056
Toys/Books
General Public
816-650-7655
www.bornlearningkc.org

Success by 6
Sunshine Center
18400 E. Salisbury Road
Independence 64056
Toys/Books
General Public
816-521-5526
www.bornlearningkc.org

Lend and Learn Toy Library
United Way
3510 E. Third Street
Joplin 64801
Books/Toys/Playroom
General Public
417-624-0153
www.unitedwaymokan.org

Success by 6 Parents as Teachers
Boone Elem. School
8817 Wornall Road
Kansas City 64114
Toys/Books
General Public
816-349-3719
www.bornlearningkc.org

Success by 6
Northgate Middle School
2117 NE 48th Street
Kansas City 64118
Toys/Books
General Public
816-413-5226
www.bornlearningkc.org

Success by 6
Freda Markley Early Childhood Center
9201 E. Bannister Road
Kansas City 64134
Toys/Books
General Public
816-316-8500
www.bornlearningkc.org

Success by 6
Oak Grove Early Childhood Center
1205 S. Salem
Oak Grove 64075
Toys/Books
General Public
816-690-3762
www.bornlearningkc.org

Success by 6
New Trails Early Childhood Center
6325 Hunter Avenue
Raytown 64133
Toys/Books
General Public
816-268-7430
www.bornlearningkc.org

Phelps County Capable Kids and
Families
1101 Hauck Drive
Rollo 65401
Books/Toys/Adaptives/Training
Special Needs, Birth to Six
573-368-2849
www.thecommunitypartnership.org

Acorn Toy Library
13201 Clayton Road
St Louis 63131
Books/Toys/Training
Enrolled Families
314-275-3558
www.principia.edu

Capable Kids and Families
1177 N. Warson Road
St. Louis 63132
Adaptive Toys & Equipment
Special Needs, Birth to Six
314-569-2211
www.slarc.org

NEBRASKA

Blair Public Library
210 S. 17th Street
Blair 68008
Books/Toy/ Kits
General Public
402-426-3617
mail@BlairPublicLibrary.com
www.libraries.ne.gov/blair

AT 4 All
1910 Meridian Avenue
Cozad 69130
Books/Adaptive Toys
Special Needs
308-784-4525
800-652-0033
www.at4all.com

Grand Island Public Library
211 N. Washington Street
Grand Island 68801
Books/Kits
General Public
308-385-5333
www.gilibrary.org

Children's Rehab Center
3004 W. Faidley Avenue
Grand Island 68803
Books/Adaptive Toys
Special Needs
308-398-5170

TreeTop Therapy
820 Village Square
Gretna 68028
Adaptive Tools & Devices
Special Needs
402-932-0747

Children's Rehab Center
2707 2nd Avenue, Suite B
Kearney 68447
Adaptive Tools & Devices
Special Needs
308-234-1278
Lindsay@kearneytherapy.com

TreeTop Therapy
620 East 25th Street
Kearney 68447
Adaptive Tools & Devices
Family Physical Therapy
Special Needs
308-455-1781
heidi.tillotson@familypt.com

Madonna Rehabilitation Hospital
5401 South Street
Lincoln 68506
Adaptive Tools & Devices
Special Needs
402-413-3676

Faith Regional Health Services
1500 Koenigstein
Norfolk 68701
Rehab Services
Special Needs/Care Providers
402-644-7348 ext. 7396
www.frhs.org/

Assistology
5300 N. 30th Street
Omaha 68110
Adaptive Toys and Devices
Special Needs/Care Providers
402-500-0667
assistologyomaha@gmail.com

Tech Tots Toy Lending Library/Children's
Hospital
8200 Dodge Street, 4th floor Scott
Pavilion
Omaha 68114
Special Needs/Care Providers
Books/Toys/Adaptives
402-955-3837

Children's Respite Care Center-
Northwest
2010 N. 88th Street
Omaha 68134
Special Needs/Care Providers
Books/Toys/Adaptives
402-496-1000

Children's Respite Care Center-
Northwest
5321 S. 138th Street
Omaha 68137
Adapted Tools/Devices
Special Needs
402-895-4000

Millard Public Schools Resource Center
6370 140th Avenue, Portable 28D
Books/Toys
Families in School District
402-715-8596
www.mps.schoolfusion.us

Papillion-La Vista Public Schools
Parents as Teachers Book & Toy Library
420 S. Washington Street
Papillion 68046
Books/Toys
Families in School District
402-537-9998
www.paplv.org

Wahoo Public Library
637 N. Maple
Wahoo 68066
Books/Toys/Games
General Public
402-443-3871

NEW JERSEY

Advancing Opportunities Toy Loan
1005 Whitehead Road, Extension Suite 1
Ewing 08638
Adaptive Toys
Special Needs
888-322-1918
atsinfo@cpofnj.org
www.drnj.org

Shirley Eves Center Toy Library/Lekotek
313 N. 10th Street
Millville 08332
Toys/Adaptives/Training/Mobile
Special Needs/At Risk
856-825-5840
mail@shirleyevescenter.org
www.shirleyevescenter.org

Toys-to-Go for Special Children
150 New Providence Road
Mountainside 07092
Toys/Adaptives
Special Needs
908-301-5478
www.childrens-specialized.org/
Resources/Toys-To-Go-Program.aspx

Children's Aid and Family Services Toy
Library
200 Robin Road
Paramus 07652
Toys/Books
Enrolled Families
Special Needs
201-261-5970
Fax 201-261-6019
www.turrell.cafsnj.org

NEW HAMPSHIRE

New Hampshire Toy Library Network
21 Madbury Road, Suite 101 (main office)
Durham 03824
Toys, Adapted Toys, Games, Kits
617-676-7995
marisa@nhtoy.org
www.nhtoy.org

NEW MEXICO

Albuquerque
YWCA Carino Toy & Resource Library
210 Truman Avenue N.E.
Books/Toys/Training/Mobile
General Public
505-254-9922
www.newmexicokids.org

San Juan Training & Technical
Assistance Center
3539 E. 30th Street
Farmington
Books/Toys/Training
General Public
505-566-3825
www.newmexicokids.org/

Project Success - Gallup
425 N. 7th Street
Gallup
Books/Toys/Training
General Public
505-722-2640
www.newmexicokids.org/

La Vida Institute
255 W. Hadley
Books/Toys/Training
Las Cruces
General Public
505-527-1149
877-527-1168
lavidainst@zianet.com
www.newmexicokids.org/

ENMU Training & Technical Assistance
Center
ENMU Education Building, Room 117
Portales
Books/Toys/Training
General Public
505-562-2850
www.newmexicokids.org/

Family Resource & Referral, Inc.
704 S. Sunset, Suite A
Books/Toys/Adaptives/Electronics/
Training
Roswell
General Public
505-622-9000, ext. 31
www.newmexicokids.org/

Toy Lending Center
6401 Richards Avenue
Santa Fe
Books/Toys/Training
General Public
505-428-1612
www.newmexicokids.org/

Toy Lending Center
6401 Richards Avenue
Santa Fe
Books/Toys/Electronics
Child Care Providers/Enrolled Families
505-428-1612
http://www.sfccnm.edu

La Familia Resource Center
513 W. 12th Street
Silver City
Books/Toys/Training
General Public
505-538-6483
www.newmexicokids.org/

Taos Family Resource Center
1335 Gusdorf Road, Suite Q
Taos
Books/Toys/Training
General Public
505-758-1395
taoskids@taosnet.com
www.newmexicokids.org/

NEW YORK

The Wonder Room
896 Saratoga Road
Ballston Lake 12019
General public
Toys/Books/ play groups
518-602-0237
www.thewonderroomschool.com

The Millicent Hearst Children's Center
Technology Resource Centers/SHARE
160 Lawrence Avenue
Brooklyn 11230
Books/Toys/Adaptives/Electronics
Special Needs
718-436-7979
www.ucpnyc.org

Toys To Go-Middle Country Public
Library
101 Eastwood Blvd.
Centereach 11720
Books/Toys/Adaptives
General Public
631-585-9393
www.mcpl.lib.ny.us

Childcare Council of Suffolk
60 Calvert Avenue
Commack 11725
Books/Toys/Adaptive Equipment
Child Care Providers
631-462-0303
www.childcaresuffolk.org

Fishkill Public Library
37 Broad Street
Fishkill 12524
Puzzles, Dolls/Books
General Public
845-896-9215
www.blodgettmemoriallibrary.org

Finger Lakes Toy Library, Inc.
Clinton West Plaza
609 West Clinton Street, Suite 106
Ithaca 14850
Toys, games, puzzles and playtimes
Serving the Finger Lakes community
607-279-2690 (Reaches President Debra
Lewis)
www.fingerlakestoylibrary.org

Heritage Play Library, Heritage Center
1 Delaware Road
Kenmore 14217
Books, Toys/Adaptives
Special Needs
716-876-3901
www.cat.buffalo.edu/triad/triadlibrary

Sullivan County Child Care Council
7 Community Lane
Liberty 12754
Books/Toys/Puppets/Theme Kits
Child Care Providers
845-292-7166
877-292-1790
www.scchildcare.com

Manhattan Technology Resource
Centers/SHARE
122 E. 23rd Street
New York 10010
Books/Toys/Adaptives/Electronics
Special Needs
212-677-7400
www.ucpnyc.org

Niagara Play Lending Center
1521 Main Street
Niagara Falls 14305
Books/Toys/Adaptives
Special Needs/Care Providers/Families
716-285-8572
800-701-4KID
www.childcareofniagra.com

Child & Family Resources Lending
Library
263 Lake Street
Penn Yan 14527
Books/Toys
Child Care Providers/Families
315-536-1134
www.cfresources.org

Childcare Council of Dutchess &
Putnam
70 Overrocker Road
Poughkeepsie 12603
Books/Toys/Equipment
Child Care Providers/Members of
Council
845-473-4141
www.childcaredutchess.org
Toy Library

Lincoln Branch of the Rochester Public
Library
851 Joseph Avenue
Rochester 14621
Books/Toys/Adaptives
General Public
585-428-8210
www3.libraryweb.org

NORTH CAROLINA

Stanly County Partnership for Children
Stanly County Commons EC Resource
Center
1000 N. First Street, Suite 8
Ablemarle 28002
Toys/Books/Games/Videos
General Public
704 982-2038 ext. 229
www.stanlypartnership.org

Mitchell Yancey Child Care R&R
Resource Library
392 East Main Street
Burnsville 28714
Toys/Books/Kits
Child Care Providers/Families
828-682-0047
www.mitchellyanceyccrr.blogspot.com

Generations-Tadpole Assistive Tech
Lending Library
205-G West E. Street
Butner 27509
Toys/Adaptive Devices
Special Needs All Ages
919-575-3093
write@tadppole.org
www.fctd.info

Charlotte Mecklenburg Library
310 N. Tryon Street
Charlotte 28202
Books/Story Kits
General Public
704-416-4662
www.cmlibrary.org

Resource Lending Library
351 Wagoner Drive, Suite 140
Fayetteville 28303
Books/Toys
Military Families Only
910-860-2277 x2502
www.fayettevillewantsyou.com

Partnership for Children Wayne Co.
800 N. Williams Street
Goldsboro 27530
Books/Toys/videos
General Public
919-753-3371
info@pfcw.org
pfcw.org/for-parents/lending-library/

Havelock-Craven Public Library - Smart
Start
301 Cunningham Blvd.
Havelock 28532
Books/Toys/Kits
General Public
252-447-7509
www.havelocklibrary.org

Toy Library & Creative Activities
Onslow County Partnership for Children
900 Dennis Road
Jacksonville 28546
Books/Toys/CDs
General Public
888-378-2470
910-938-0336
www.onslowkids.org/resource-center.
php

Duplin County Partnership for Children
Lending Library
149 Limestone Road
Kenansville 28349
Books/Kits
General Public
910-296-2000
www.dcpfc.org

Stokes Partnership for Children
Lending Library
151 Jefferson Church Road
King 27021
Books/Toys/Kits
General Public
336-985-2676 x116
www.stokespfc.com/library

Harnett County Child Care Resource
Library
126 Alexander Drive, Suite 300
Lillington 27546
Books/Toys/Kits
General Public
910-814-6039
www.hcccrr.weebly.com

South Piedmont College – Smart Start
Resource Center
4209 Old Charlotte Highway
Monroe 28110
Books/Toys
General Public
704-290-5894
www.unionsmartstart.org

Craven Smart Start Resource Library
2111-F Neuse Blvd.
New Bern 28560
Books/Toys/Play Sessions
General Public
252-671-0689
www.cravensmartstart.org

Hoke Co. Resource Lending Library
1089 E. Central Avenue
Raeford 28376
Books/Toys/Training
Child Care Providers/Families
910-904-6688
www.ccpfc.org

Onslow Kids Resource Lending Library
8304 Richlands Highway, Suite 1&2
Richlands 28574
Books/Toys
General Public
910-324-6590
www.onslowkids.org/resource-center.
php

Coalition for Families CCR&R Resource
Library
507 North Steele Street
Sanford 27330
Books/Toys
General Public in Lee County
919-774-8144 x 209
www.coalitionforfamilies.org

Partnership for Kids North Topsail
Shores
Baptist Church
08 Old Folkstone Road
Sneads Ferry 28460
Books/Toys
General Public
910-327-1161
. www.onslowkids.org/resource-center.
php

Partnership for Children
686 Corbett Avenue, Suite 13
Swansboro 28584
Books/Toys
General Public
910-326-4752
www.onslowkids.org/resource-center.
php

Center for Assistive Technology Library
Natural Sciences Modular Unit, Room 1026
Walton Drive
Wilmington 28403
Adaptive Toys/Equipment
Special Needs
910-962-2579
assistive@uncw.edu
www.uncw.edu/ed/assist

Smart Start Puzzles Center
Family Resource Room
3534 S. College Road, Suite F
Wilmington 28412
Books/Kits
Child Care Providers/Families in New Hanover Co.
910-815-3731
877-722-7857
www.newhanoverkids.org

The Partnership Resource Lending Library
1084 NC Highway, 86 North
Yanceyville 27379
Books/Kits/Toys
General Public, Caswell County
336-694-1538
ccp4child@esinc.net
www.caswellchildren.org

OHIO

United Disability Services
Toy & Resource Center
701 S. Main Street
Akron 44311
Toys/ Resources/ Adaptives
General Public
330-762-9755
www.udsakron.org

Rodman Public Library
215 E. Broadway
Alliance 44601
Books/Toys/Electronics
General Public
330-821-2665
www.rodmanlibrary.com

Northwest State Community College Library
22600 State Route 34
Archbold 43502
Books. Toys/Adaptives/Training
Student population
419-267-5511 ext. 274
lib@northweststate.edu
www.northwestsate.edu

Ashtabula County District Library
335 W. 44th Street
Ashtabula 44004
Books/Toys
General Public
440-997-9341
www.acdl.info

Bay Village Branch Library CCPL
502 Cahoon Road
Bay Village 44140
Books/Toys/Adaptives
General Public
440-871-6392
www.cuyahoga.lib.oh.us

Beachwood Branch Library CCPL
25501 Shaker Blvd.
Beachwood 44122
Books/Toys/Adaptives
General Public
216-831-6868
www.cuyahoga.lib.oh.us

Southeast Branch Library CCPL
70 Columbus Road
Bedford 44146
Books/Toys/Adaptives
General Public
440-439-4997
www.cuyahoga.lib.oh.us

Berea Branch Library CCPL
7 Berea Commons
Berea 44017
Books/Toys/Adaptives
General Public
440-234-5475
www.cuyahoga.lib.oh.us

Brecksville Branch Library CCPL
9089 Brecksville Road
Brecksville 44141
Books/Toys/Adaptives
General Public
440-526-1102
www.cuyahoga.lib.oh.us

Brook Park Branch Library CCPL
6155 Engle Road
Brook Park 44142
Books/Toys/Adaptives
General Public
216-267-5250
www.cuyahoga.lib.oh.us

Brooklyn Branch Library CCPL
4480 Ridge Road
Brooklyn 44144
Books/Toys/Adaptives
General Public
216-398-4600
www.cuyahoga.lib.oh.us

Medina County Public Library-
Brunswick Branch
SHC Toy Lending
3649 Center Road
Brunswick 44212
Books/Toys/Adaptives
General Public
330-273-4150
www.medina.lib.oh.us

Toy Lending Library-Crawford Co DD
1650 E. Southern Avenue
Bucyrus 44820
Books/Toys/Adaptives/Training
Special Needs/Care Providers
419-562-3321

Bucyrus Public Library
200 East Mansfield Street
Books/Adaptives
General Public
419-562-7327
www.youseemore.com/bucyrus

Puskarich Public Library
200 E. Market Street
Cadiz 43907
Books/Toys
General Public
740-942-2623
www.harrison.lib.oh.us

ECRC Toy Lending Library
3114 Cleveland Avenue NW
Canton 44709
Toy Kits/Books/Training
Stark Co. Early Childhood Providers
330-491-3272
www.ecresourcecenter.org

Dorcas Carey Public Library
236 East Findley Street
Carey 43316
Books/Toys
General Public
419-396-7921
www.dorcascarey.org

Chagrin Falls Branch Library CCPL
100 E. Orange Street
Chagrin Falls Village 44022
Books/Toys
General Public
440-247-3556
www.cuyahoga.lib.oh.us

Play Library
1517 Elm Street
Cincinnati 45202
Game & Toy Lending Library
General Public
513-407-7045
hello@playlibrary.org
www.playlibrary.org

Rubinstein Toy Library for Special
Children
3430 Burnet Avenue
Cincinnati 45229
Books/Toys/Adaptives
General Public
513-636-4626
800-344-2462 ext. 64626
www.cincinnatichildrens.org/service/r/
rubinstein-library

Nationwide Children's Hospital
Family Resource Center Toy Library
C1840
700 Children's Drive
Columbus 43205
Toys/Adaptives
Families at the Hospital
614-722-2252
www.nationwidechildrens.org/family-
resource-center

Toy & Technology Library at Nisonger
Center
Room 286 McCampbell Hall
1581 Dodd Drive
Columbus 43210
Toys/Adaptives
Special Needs Families
614-688-3431
http://nisonger.osu.edu/clinics-services/
toy-technology-library/

Southview Children & Family Center
Library
25 Thorpe Drive
Dayton 45420
Books/Toys/Adaptives/Electronics
Special Needs Birth to Three- Enrolled
937-258-1446
www.mcbdds.org

United Way Strengthening Families Toy
Library
74 W. William Street
Delaware 43015
Toys
General Public
614-436-8929
www.DelawareCountyFamilies.org

Preble County District Library
El Dorado Branch
150 N. Main Street
El Dorado 45321
Books/Adaptives
General Public
937-273-4933
www.pcdl.lib.oh.us

Murray Ridge Center LCBDD
EC Lending Library
1091 Infirmary Road
Elyria 44035
Adaptive Toys/Equipment
Special Needs in Lorain County
440-284-3655
www.murrayridgecenter.org

Fairview Park Branch Library CCPL
21255 Lorain Road
Fairview Park 44126
Books/Toys
General Public
440-333-4700
www.cuyahoga.lib.oh.us

Garfield Heights Branch Library CCPL
5409 Turney Road
Garfield Heights 44125
Books/Toys
General Public
216-475-8178
www.cuyahoga.lib.oh.us

Gates Mills Branch Library CCPL
1491 Chagrin River Road
Gates Mills 44040
Books/Toys
General Public
440-423-4808
www.cuyahoga.lib.oh.us

Geneva Public Library
860 Sherman Street
Geneva 44041
Books/Toys
General Public
440-466-4521
www.acdl.info

Katelyn's Kloset
3730 Trueman Court
Hilliard 43026
Adaptive Toys and Capability Switches
Special Needs Children, Therapists,
Teachers and Professionals
614-526-8936
www.katelynskloset.org

Highland County District Library
10 Willettsville Pike
Hillsboro 45113
Books/Toys
General Public
937-393-3114
www.highlandco.org

HTCT Parent Resource Room
8001 Township Road 574
Holmesville 44633
Books/Toys/Adaptives
Special Needs
330-674-8045
www.holmesdd.org

Independence Branch Library CCPL
6361 Selig Drive
Independence 44131
Books/Toys
General Public
216-447-0160
www.cuyahoga.lib.oh.us

Mathew's Lending Library
15528 Madison Avenue
Lakewood 44107
Adaptives/Equipment
Special Needs
216-226-3669
www.matthewslendinglibrary.org/

Fairfield County District Library
219 North Broad Street
Lancaster 43130
Adaptives/Books
General Public
740-653-2745
www.fcdlibrary.org

Wagnalls Memorial Library
150 E. Columbus Street
Lithopolis 43136
Adaptives/Books
General Public
614-837-4765
www.wagnalls.org

Lodi Branch Medina Public Library
SHC Toy Lending
635 Wooster Street
Lodi 44254
Books/Toys/Adaptives
General Public
330-948-1885
www.medina.lib.oh.us

Eastgate Early Childhood Center
2121 Ashland Street NE
Louisville 44641
Adaptives/Toys
Families Enrolled
330-479-3440

Maple Heights Branch Library CCPL
5225 Library Lane
Maple Heights 44137
Books/Toys
General Public
216-475-5000
www.cuyahoga.lib.oh.us

Mayfield Branch Library CCPL
500 Som Center Road
Mayfield Village 44143
Books/Toys
General Public
440-473-0350
www.cuyahoga.lib.oh.us

Medina Public Library
SHC Toy Lending
210 S. Broadway Street
Medina 44256
Books/Toys/Adaptives/Theme Boxes
General Public
330-725-0588
www.medina.lib.oh.us

Buckeye Branch Medina Public Library
SHC Toy Lending
6625 Wolfe Road
Medina 44256
Books/Toys/Adaptives
General Public
330-725-4415
www.medina.lib.oh.us

Highland Branch Medina Public Library
SHC Toy Lending
4160 Ridge Road
Medina 44256
Books/Toys/Adaptives
General Public
330-278-4271
www.medina.lib.oh.us

Middleburg Heights Branch Library
CCPL
15600 E. Bagley Road
Middleburg Heights 44130
Books/Toys
General Public
440-234-3600
www.cuyahoga.lib.oh.us

New Bremen Public Library
45 W. Washington Street
New Bremen 45869
Books/Adaptives
General Public
419-629-2158
www.auglaize.oplin.org

New Knoxville Public Library
304 S. Main Street
New Knoxville 45871
Books/Adaptives
General Public
419-753-2724
www.auglaize.oplin.org

North Olmstead Branch Library CCPL
27403 Lorain Road
North Olmstead 44070
Books/Toys
General Public
440-777-6211
www.cuyahoga.lib.oh.us

North Royalton Branch Library CCPL
5071 Wallings Road
North Royalton 44133
Books/Toys
General Public
440-237-3800
www.cuyahoga.lib.oh.us

Olmstead Falls Branch Library CCPL
8100 Mapleway Drive
Olmstead Falls 44138
Books/Toys
General Public
440-235-1150
www.cuyahoga.lib.oh.us

Parma Ridge Branch Library CCPL
5850 Ridge Road
Parma 44129
Books/Toys
General Public
440-888-4300
www.cuyahoga.lib.oh.us

Parma Heights Branch Library
6206 Pearl Road
Parma Heights 44130
Books/Toys
General Public
440-884-2313
www.cuyahoga.lib.oh.us

Parma Snow Branch Library CCPL
2121 Snow Road
Parma 44134
Books/Toys
General Public
216-661-4240
www.cuyahoga.lib.oh.us

Parma South Branch Library CCPL
7335 Ridge Road
Parma 44129
Books/Toys
440-885-5362
General Public
www.cuyahoga.lib.oh.us

Orange Branch Library CCPL
31300 Chagrin Blvd.
Pepper Pike 44124
Books/Toys
General Public
216-831-4282
www.cuyahoga.lib.oh.us

Meigs County Public District Library
216 W. Main Street
Pomeroy 45769
Books/Adaptives
General Public
740-992-5813
www.meigs.lib.oh.us

Happy Day School-Lending Library
2500 Brady Lake
Ravenna 44266
Books/Toys/Adaptives/Electronics
Special Needs
330-678-2400
www.portagedd.org

Richmond Heights Branch Library CCPL
5235 Wilson Mills Road
Richmond Heights 44143
Books/Toys
General Public
440-449-2666
www.cuyahoga.lib.oh.us

Rock Creek Public Library
2988 High Street
Rock Creek 44084
Books/Toys
General Public
440-563-3340
www.rockcreek.lib.oh.us

Saint Paris Public Library
127 E. Main Street
Saint Paris 43072
Books/Toys
General Public
937-663-4349
www.stparispubliclibrary.org

SHC Toy Lending Library
4283 Paradise Road
Seville 44273
Books/Toys/Adaptives
General Public/Special Needs
330-722-1900
877-546-8568
shc@shc-medina.org
www.shc-medina.org

Seville Branch Medina Public Library
SHC Toy Lending
North Center Street
Seville 44273
Books/Toys/Adaptives
General Public
330-769-2852
www.medina.lib.oh.us

Amos Memorial Public Library
230 East North Street
Sidney 45365
Toys/Puppets/Adaptives
General Public
937-492-8354
www.amos.lib.oh.us

Solon Branch Library CCPL
34125 Portz Pkwy.
Solon 44139
Books/Toys
General Public
440-248-8777
www.cuyahoga.lib.oh.us

South Euclid-Lyndhurst Branch Library
CCPL
4645 Mayfield Road
South Euclid 44121
Books/Toys
General Public
216-382-4880
www.cuyahoga.lib.oh.us

St. Mary's Public Library
140 S. Chestnut Street
St. Mary 45885
Books/Toys/Adaptives
General Public
419-394-7471
www.auglaize.oplin.org

Public Library of Steubenville-Schiappa
Branch
4141 Mall Drive
Steubenville 43952
Books/Adaptives
General Public
740-264-6166
www.steubenville.lib.oh.us

Strongsville Branch Library CCPL
18700 Westwood Drive
Strongsville 44136
Books/Toys
General Public
440-238-5530
www.cuyahoga.lib.oh.us

Champaign County Library
1060 Scioto Street
Urbana 43078
Books/Adaptives
General Public
937-653-3811
www.champaign.lib.oh.us

Wadsworth Public Library-SHC Toy
Lending Library
132 Broad Street
Wadsworth 44281
Books/Toys/Adaptives
General Public
330-334-5761
www.wadsworthlibrary.com/children/

Auglaize County Public District Library
203 Perry Street
Wapakoneta 45895
Books/Adaptives
General Public
419-738-2921
www.auglaize.oplin.org

Warrensville Branch Library CCPL
4415 Northfield Road
Warrensville Heights 44128
Books/Toys
General Public
216-464-5280
www.cuyahoga.lib.oh.us

White Memorial Library
108 E. Wapakoneta Street
Waynesfield 45896
Books/Toys/Adaptives
General Public
419-568-5851
www.auglaize.oplin.org

Wayne County Public Library
200 West Liberty Street
Wooster 44691
Books/Toys
General Public
330-262-0916
www.wcpl.info

OKLAHOMA

Blanchard Public Library
205 NE 10th Street
Blanchard 73010
Literacy Kits with toys
General Public
405-485-2275
pioneerlibrarysystem.org/blanchard

Child Care Finders Toy Lending Library
114 S. Independence
Enid 73701
Toys/Books/Games/Videos
Child Care Providers/General Public
800-401-3463
ccf@cdsaok.org
www.childcarefinder.org

Mcloud Public Library
133 North Main
Mcloud 74851
Literacy Kits with Toys
General Public
405-964-2960
pioneerlibrarysystem.org/mcloud

Moore Public Library
225 South Howard
Moore 73160
Literacy Kits with Toys
General Public
405-793-5100
pioneerlibrarysystem.org/moore

New Castle Public Library
705 NW 10th
New Castle 73065
Literacy Kits with Toys
General Public
405-387-5076
pioneerlibrarysystem.org/newcastle

Noble Public Library
204 N. 5th Street
Noble 73068
Literacy Kits with Toys
General Public
405-872-5713
pioneerlibrarysystem.org/noble

Norman Public Library Central
225 North Webster
Norman 73069
Literacy Kits with Toys
General Public
405-701-2600
pioneerlibrarysystem.org/Norman

Norman Public Library West
300 Norman Center
Norman 73072
Literacy Kits with Toys
General Public
405-701-2644
pioneerlibrarysystem.org/westnorman

Rainbow Fleet CCR&R Resource Center
3024 Paseo
Oklahoma City 73103
Books/Toys/Training
Child Care Providers/ Families
405-521-1426
800-438-0008
www.rainbowfleet.org/

Oklahoma Library for the Blind &
Physically Handicapped
300 NE 18th Street
Oklahoma City 73105
Toys/Braille books/Educational aids
Physical disabilities
800-523-0288
olbph@okdrs.gov
www.library.state.ok.us

Southwest Oklahoma City Library
2201 SW 134th
Oklahoma City 73107
Literacy Kits with Toys
General Public
405-979-2200
pioneerlibrarysystem.org/hometowns/
sokc

Ability Connection
10400 Greenbriar Place, Suite 101
Oklahoma City 73159
Adapted toys/Equipment
Special needs
405-759-3562
800-827-2289
okc@abilityconnectionoklahoma.org
www.abilityconnectionoklahoma.org

Purcell Public Library
919 N. 9th Street
Purcell 73080
Literacy Kits with Toys
General Public
405-527-5546
pioneerlibrarysystem.org/purcell

Shawnee Public Library
101 North Philadelphia
Shawnee 74081
Literacy Kits with Toys
General Public
405-275-6353
pioneerlibrarysystem.org/shawnee

Oklahoma State Ed & Teaching Library
101 Willard Hall, Whitehurst Lane
Stillwater 74074
Books/Toys/Games/Kits
Students/Faculty/Professionals in
Community
405-744-9776
405-744-6310
Lib-dls@okstate.edu
www.library.okstate.edu

Oklahoma State University/ Dept. of
Wellness AbleTech
1514 W. Hall of Fame
Stillwater 74078
Adapted toys/ Equipment
Special Needs
405-744-9748
abletech@okstate.edu
www.ok.gov/abletech

Tecumseh Public Library
114 North Broadway
Tecumseh 74873
Literacy Kits with Toys
General Public
405-598-5955
pioneerlibrarysystem.org/tecumseh

Child Care Resource Center
16 E. 16th Street, Suite 202
Tulsa 74119
Books/Toys/DVDs
General Public
918-834-2273
info@ccrctulsa.org
www.ccrctulsa.org

OREGON

Polk County CCR&R Lending Library
1610 Monmouth Street
Independence 97351
Toys/Books/Furniture
Child Care Providers
800-289-5533 (must call for an
Appointment)
www.mwvcaa.org

Southside Swap and Play
5239 SE Woodstock Blvd.
Portland 97206
Toys
General Public
971-266-3023
www.southsideswapandplay.org

Woodland Swap 'n Play
704 NE Dekum Street
Portland 97211
Toys
General Public
503-269-4943
www.woodlawnswapnplay.org

PDX Toy Library
3520 SE Yamhill Street
Portland 97214
Toys
General Public
503-477-0338
www.facebook.com/PDXToyLibrary

Marion County CCR&R Lending Library
2475 Center Street NE
Salem 97301
Toys/Books/Furniture
Child Care Providers
800-289-5533 (must call for an
Appointment)
www.mwvcaa.org

PENNSYLVANIA

McBride Memorial Library
500 N. Market St.
Berwick 18603
Toys, Materials
General Public
570-752-2241
info@mcbridelibrary.org
www.mcbridelibrary.org

BU Toy Library
400 E. Second St.
1247 McCormick Center for Human
Studies
Bloomsburg 17815
Toys/Games/Books
Community Professionals, Students at
BU
570-389-3915
butoylibrary@bloom.edu
butoylibrary.bloomu.edu/

Elizabethville Area Library
80 N. Market St.
Elizabethville 17023
Toy Kits/Puzzles/Games
General Public
717-362-9825
WebMailEV@DCLS.org
www.dcls.org

McCormick Riverfront Library
101 Walnut St.
Harrisburg 17101
Toy Kits/Puzzles/Games
General Public
717-234-4976
WebMailMRL@DCLS.org
www.dcls.org

Kline Library
530 South 29th St.
Harrisburg 17104
Toy Kits/Puzzles/Games
General Public
717-234-3934
WebMailKL@DCLS.org
www.dcls.org

East Shore Area Library
4501 Ethel St.
Harrisburg 17109
Toy Kits/Puzzles/Games
General Public
717-652-9380
WebMailESA@DCLS.org
www.dcls.org

Madeline L. Olewine Memorial Library
2410 North Third St.
Harrisburg 17110
Toy Kits/Puzzles/Games
General Public
717-232-7286
WebMailMOM@DCLS.org
www.dcls.org

Keystone Assistive Tech & Toy Library
3700 Vartan Way
Harrisburg 17110
Adaptive Toys/Equipment
Special Needs
717-525-7795
www.keystonehumanservices.org/

Wm & Marion Alexander Fam. Library
200 West Second St.
Hummelstown 17036
Toy Kits/Puzzles/Games
General Public
717-566-0949
WebMailAFL@DCLS.org
www.dcls.org

Schreiber Pediatric Rehab Center
625 Community Way
Lancaster 17603
Adaptive Toys/ Resource Information
Special Needs
717-393-0425
info@schreiberpediatric.org
www.schreiberpediatric.org

Playworks Toy Lending Library
St. Francis University DiSepio Bldg.
Loretto 15940
Toy Kits/Puzzles/Games
General Public
814-472-2749
www.francis.edu/Toy-Lending-Library

Northern Dauphin Library
683 Main St.
Lykens 17048
Toy Kits/Puzzles/Games
General Public
717-523-0340
WebMailND@DCLS.org
www.dcls.org

Meadville Public Library
848 North Main St.
Meadville 16335
Toy Kits, Puzzles
General Public
814-336-1773
www.meadvillelibrary.org

Johnson Memorial Library
799 East Center St.
Millersburg 17061
Toy Kits, Puzzles, Games
General Public
717-692-2658
mkattner@dcls.org
www.dcls.org

Orangeville Public Library
301 Mill St.
Orangeville 17859
Adaptive Equipment
Special Needs
570-683-5354
orangevillelibrary@pa.metrocast.net
www.orangevillelibrary.org

PA Assistive Technology Lending Library
Temple University
Philadelphia 19122
State-wide, request materials through
website
Adaptives/Toys/Electronics
Special Needs
215-204-1356
atinfo@temple.edu
www.disabilities.temple.edu

PARK Resource Center & Toy Library
580 Old Rt. 322
Philipsburg 16866
Toys/Kits/Videos
General Public
814-342-5678
www.cenclear.org

Pittsburgh Toy Lending Library & Play
Space
5401 Centre Avenue, Rear
Pittsburgh 15232
Toys/Indoor Play Space/Parenting
Resources
General Public
412-682-4430
ptll@pghtoys.org
www.pghtoys.org

UCP Lekotek of NE PA
425 Wyoming Ave.
Scranton 18503
Toys, Indoor Play Space, Parenting
Resources
Special Needs
570-587-5892
www.ucpnepa.org

Indian Valley Public Library
100 E. Church Ave.
Telford 18969
Toys, Books
General Public
215-723-9109
www.ivpl.org

Giggles & Tickles Toybrary
1024 East Willow Grove Avenue
Wyndmoor 19038
Toy Lending, Educational Classes, Toy
Sales, Parties
Infant – 6 yrs.
215-233-1244
meldeldol@gmail.com
www.gigglesandticklestoybrary.com

Lakin Toy Library
555 Warwick Dr.
Wyomissing 19610
Toys/Materials
General Public
610-375-6034
ohebsholom.org/sprouts-and-music/

SOUTH DAKOTA

Family Resource Network
Medary Ave & Harvey Dunn Street
SDSU Box 2218
Brookings
Books/Toys/Training/Mobile
Child Care Providers/Enrolled Families
605-688-5730
800-354-8238
www.sdstate.edu/tll/frn
Family Child Care Program
1000 Ellsworth Street
Ellsworth AFB
Toys
Child Care Providers
605-385-4330

TEXAS

Any Baby Can
1121 E. 7th Street
Austin
Toys/Training
Special Needs
512-454-3743
800-672-0238
www.abcaus.org

Tobrary Austin
7817 Rockwood Lane, Suite 101
Austin, TX 78757
512-765-4174
toybraryaustin.com

Toy Tech
4500 Bissonnet, Suite 340
Bellaire
Books/Toys/Adaptives/Videos/Training
Special Needs
713-838-9050 or 346-330-3852
jlrodriguez@eastersealshouston.org
www.eastersealshouston.org/

F.I.R.S.T. Place
315 Washington Avenue
Waco
Parent education & support/parent-child
activities/lending library
Birth to five/low income/single parents/
Spanish speaking/teenage and young
mothers
254-752-3961

UTAH

Parent Information Resource Center/
PIRC
1150 S. Main Street
Orem
Books/Toys/Training
Parents/School Administrators/Teachers
801-225-7440
parents@familycenter-pirc.org
www.utahcountyonline.org/dept/
healthwic2/site/community-resources/
Learn%20More_Comm%20Res/LM_
CommRes_1284ChildrenFamServices.
html

VIRGINIA

Blue Ridge Regional Library
Bassett Branch
3969 Fairystone Park Hwy.
Bassett 24055
Books/ Literacy Kits
General Public
276-629-2426
bassett@brrl.lib.va.us
www.brrl.lib.va.us

Blue Ridge Regional Library Martinsville
310 East Church Street
Martinsville 24112
Books/Literacy Kits/Toys
General Public
276-403-5430
martinsville@brrl.lib.va.us
www.brrl.lib.va.us

Easter Seals UCP NC & VA
Lekotek Center
201 E. Main Street
Salem 24153
Toys/Adaptives
Special Needs-Enrolled Families
540-777-7325
nc.eastersealsucp.com/services/lekotek

WISCONSIN

Toy Library
707 Quay Street
Manitowoc
Books/Toys/Training
General Public
920-683-4863, ext. 6
www.manitowoclibrary.org

Marshfield Children's Lekotek
Center
611 St. Joseph Hospital
Marshfield
Books/Toys / Adaptives /
Training
Special Needs
715-387-7885
800-335-5251

Toy & Equipment Lending
Library
38 Broad Street, Suite 120
Oshkosh
Toys / Adaptives / Electronics /
 Mobile
Special Needs
920-424-4071
800-261-1895

Toybrary
710 N. 8th Street
Sheboygan
Books / Toys / Adaptives /
Training
General Public
920-459-3400, ext. 3404
http://www.meadpubliclibrary.org/

Learning Resource Center - The Toy
Barn
107 S. 4th Avenue
Sturgeon Bay
Toys
General Public
920-743-6578

Toy & Book Subscription Memberships

Bookroo
Picture book membership
Bookroo.com
Membership starts at $22.99 monthly

Cricket Crate
Early educational projects
KiwiCo.com
Membership starts at $20 monthly

Green Kids Craft
Themed STEAM projects (3 y.o. and up)
Cratejoy.com
Membership starts at $19 monthly

Hello Bible
Creative and faith-filled activities
Hellobible.org
Membership starts at $21.90 monthly

Hoppi Box
Developmental toy subscription
Hoppibox.com
Membership starts at $66/quarterly

Little Pnuts
Exploratory toys for imaging, creating &
playing
Littlepnuts.com
Membership starts at $25 monthly or
$20 (12-month subscription)

Milestones ABC
Educational toys, book, & clothes
Milestonesabc.com
Membership starts at $59/quarterly

Tadpole Crate
Project-based activities for toddlers
KiwiCo.com
Multiple membership options starting
at $17 monthly

Tittletot (not a membership, parents
purchase boxes)
Montessori-inspired educational kits
Tittletot.com
Kits start at $24.95

The Story Box
Book club designed for toddlers
Jointhestorybox.com
Membership starts at $20 monthly

Appendix G: Resources to Locate Licensed Speech and Language Pathologists

American Speech-Language-Hearing Association is a national association for licensed speech and language pathologist. Each state has individual associations that represent local speech-language pathologist, providing parent resources and current topics relating to speech and language pathology.

U.S. National Association

American Speech-Language-Hearing Association
www.asha.org

State Associations

Alabama
www.alabamashaa.org

Alaska
www.aksha.org

Arkansas
www.arksha.org

Arizona
www.arsha.org

California
www.csha.org

Colorado
www.cshassoc.org

Connecticut
ctspeechandhearing.org

District of Columbia
www.dcsha.org

Delaware
www.dsha.org

Florida
www.flasha.org

Georgia
www.gsha.org

Hawaii
www.hsha.wildapricot.org

Idaho
www.idahosha.org

Iowa
www.isha.org

Illinois
www.ishail.org

Indiana
www.islha.org

Kansas
www.ksha.org

Kentucky
www.ksha.info

Louisiana
www.lsha.org

Maine
www.maineslp.org

Maryland
www.mdslha.org

Massachusetts
www.mshahearsay.org

Michigan
www.michiganspeechhearing.org

Minnesota
www.mnsha.org

Mississippi
www.mshausa.org

Montana
www.mshaonline.org

Nebraska
www.nslha.org

Nevada
www.nvsha.org

New Hampshire
www.nhslha.org

New Mexico
www.nmsha.org

New York
www.nysslha.org

North Carolina
www.ncshla.org

North Dakota
www.ndslha.org

Ohio
www.ohioslha.org

Oklahoma
www.oslha.org

Oregon
www.oregonspeechandhearing.org

Pennsylvania
www.psha.org

Rhode Island
www.risha.info

South Carolina
www.scsha.org

South Dakota
www.sdslha.org

Tennessee
www.taaslp.org

Texas
www.txsha.org

Utah
www.ushaonline.net

Vermont
www.vsha.org

Virginia
www.shav.org

Washington
www.wslha.org

West Virginia
www.wvsha.org

Wisconsin
www.wisha.org

Wyoming
www.wyosha.org

Bibliography

American Speech and Hearing Association (2008). Roles and responsibilities of speech-language pathologists in early intervention: guidelines. Available from www.asha.org/policy.

California Department of Education (2019, September 10). Foundation: Cause-and-Effect. Retrieved from https://www.cde.ca.gov/sp/cd/re/itf09cogdevfdcae.asp

Cortese, R. (2017, November 27). Helping toddlers expand language skills. Retrieved from https://playandlearn.com/importanttips/helping-toddlers-expand-language-skills/

Mori, F., Naghsh, F. A., & Tezuka, T. (2014). The effect of music on the level of mental concentration and its temporal change. Presented at the CSEDU 6th International Conference on Computer Supported Education. Retrieved from https://pdfs.semanticscholar.org/edef/995d4e21663ea31480907af37222e7b32297.pdf

National Center on Birth Defects and Developmental Disabilities (2019, August 27). Signs and symptoms of autism spectrum disorder. Retrieved from https://www.cdc.gov/ncbddd/

Schellenberg, E. G., (2005). "Music and cognitive abilities," Current Direction in Psychological Science, 14(6), 317-320.

Sualy, A., Yount, S., Kelly-Vancel, L, & Ryalls, B. (2011). "Using a play intervention to improve the play skills of children with a language delay." International Journal of Psychology: A Biopsychosocial Approach, 9, 105-122.

Glossary

American Sign Language (ASL): is a complete, natural language that has the same linguistic properties as spoken languages. ASL is expressed by movements of the hands or face.

Attention: the ability to focus while filtering out irrelevant information in order to practice a specific task

Cause and effect play: the understanding that one event brings about another

Communication: the exchanging and receiving information, thoughts, feelings and ideas

Crash-and-bang play: play interaction that involved repetitiously making two objects collide for long periods of time

Expressive language: imparting ideas, thoughts and feelings to another individual

Focus: directed attention toward an activity

Parallel play: describing actions during play

Picture exchange system (PECS): a form of augmented and alternative communication

Play: engaging in an activity for recreation and enjoyment

Play modeling: providing an example of play for imitation or comparison

Play runners: when a child flees the play area from a play partner to find different activity for independent play

Receptive language: how a person comprehends, processes, and understands language or words spoken to them

Reinforce: rewarding or providing praise to a person in order for an action to reoccur

Sensory: related to the process that organizes sensation from one's own body and the environment, thus making it possible to use the body effectively within the environment

Stimulating: encouraging or arousing interest or enthusiasm

About The Author

Cherina L. Williams, M.Ed., CCC-SLP is a passionate pediatric speech and language pathologist, podcast host of "I've Got This Kid," homeschooler of two and wife of one, who resides in the San Francisco Bay Area, where she loves to walk, play, write and aspire others to maximize their potential. Before Cherina chose working with children as a career choice, she always exhibited a love and a passion relating to children. She has voluntarily served in various roles in the Children's Ministry for over 20 years.

Cherina received her undergraduate degree at Clark Atlanta University in 2006 in Speech Communication. Upon completion of her degree, she worked in academia before enrolling in graduate school to pursue a master's degree at University of West Georgia in 2008. Throughout her tenure in graduate school, Cherina continued to establish herself as a pediatric speech and language pathologist, taking advantage of various externships in the Atlanta area.

After completing graduate school in 2011, Cherina worked at Children's Hospital & Research Center, Oakland (now CHRCO & UCSF Benioff) in their outpatient clinic as a Pediatric Speech and Language Pathologist, under the supervision of Robin Violette. In 2013, Cherina started a private practice, "I Heart Speech Therapy," where she subspecialized serving the birth-to-three population.

Understanding the unique needs of serving the birth-to-three population, Cherina learned the true value of finding the balance between educating parents, teaching parents how to generalize therapeutic goals and creating effective avenues to ensure that client goals were being met. Cherina learned that parents wanted answers about how to be an asset for their child's growth and development, so she began writing the most frequently asked questions to try to serve the broader audience.

"It is my ultimate goal to help families maximize their relationship with their child, using play as a medium."

-Cherina Williams,
M.Ed., CCC-SLP

connect with me

cherina
Williams
M.Ed., CCC SLP

Podcast

www.ivegotthiskid.com

PODBEAN

APPLE

GOOGLE PLAY

IHEART RADIO

STICHER

YOUTUBE

Web

I Heart
speech
therapy

www.iheartspeechtherapy.com

I've Got This Kid
PODCAST
www.ivegotthiskid.com

Socials

@ivegotthiskid_podcast

Cherina Williams

Cherina Williams

professional offerings

cherina
Williams
M.Ed., CCC-SLP

Language Milestone Movement
What should I expect?

Did you know that foundational language development for the birth to 3 population can have a lasting impact on social skills, cognition, problem solving, and long-term academic skills??? Did you know that learning understanding early language development can not only excel your learners, but also bridge the gap with sluggish speakers??? Get ahead of the game by learning these milestones to benefit your learning community!

-Language Development Milestones (Receptive & Expressive)
-Characteristics of Language Delays   -Natural Strategies to Decrease Gaps

Behavior Busters
Distinguishing between language delay or learned behaviors?

During the language BOOM, toddlers are learning to use their words to replace crying. When toddlers are not using words to communicate, they are using behaviors to help compensate. These behaviors can impact the classroom, educators, families as well as impact your student's ability to learn. Avoid getting caught in behaviors and learn how to bust unwanted behaviors while creating a healthy learning environment!

-Characteristics of Language Delays   -Associated Behaviors in Language Delays
-Strategies for Support   -Red Flag Behaviors

Classroom Goals
Managing Language Goals in the Class

With inclusion on the rise, educators are not always equipped to handle day-to-day responsibilities as well as how to include all learners in the classroom environment. Learn simple, easy-to-follow strategies to overcome these hurdles with ease. Tool your educators up to create a healthy learning community!!!

-Supporting the Language Delayed Child   -Collaborating with Families
-Fun, Foundational Reading Techniques   - Managing Language Goals in the Class

parent webinar offerings

cherina
Williams
M.Ed . CCC SLP

Steps To
Intentional Parenting

Parenting is one of the most rewarding, demanding and challenging tasks faced! It is easy to feel as if balancing life, work, and home is simply impossible! However, it does not have to be...you can learn how to master intentional parenting by learning how to tailor life for your specific family needs. With a few simple tweaks, you can learn all the foundational essentials needed to be your best parenting you!

-Steps to create an organized daily schedule   -Steps into BUSTING unwanted behavior
-Steps to establish boundaries   -Steps into Amazing Play

Milestone Movement
What should I expect?

When does eye-contact start? At what age should my sugar respond to their name? How many words at age 2? New parents, why wait until entering the doctors office to learn the inter workings of your sugars speech language development? Get ahead of the game by learning milestones from an EXPERT! Learn how to tailor the language learning environment based on your sugars need in a fun, practical, proactive way!

-Speech and language milestones from birth to 3   -Fosteting Healthy Communication
-Learning Style Play Techniques   -Signs of a Sluggish Speaker

Personalized Touch
Tailoring You

Want a dynamic personalized, tailored touch to meet your specific family needs in an interpersonal way? Let Chernia get your family tool'd up. Participants can choose from "Intentional Parenting," "What Should I Expect," or additional topics listed:

-Understanding & Engaging Neurodivergent Sugar   -Parenting on the Same Page
-Fun, Foundational Reading Techniques   -Play Space Reorganization
-Communicating with Language Delayed Sugars   -Toy Selection to Foster Healthy Learning
-Sensory Processing Disorder Tips, Tools, and Tricks

CPSIA information can be obtained
at www.ICGtesting.com
Printed in the USA
BVHW012254240122
627041BV00005B/41

9 781734 520613